HERO OF DARIEN

HERO OF DARIEN

The Story of Vasco Núñez de Balboa

By

MAXINE SHORE

and

M. M. OBLINGER

LONGMANS, GREEN AND CO.

NEW YORK · TORONTO

1941

CONTENTS

vii

FOREWORD

"GOLD! ADVENTURE! STRANGE LANDS ACROSS THE SEA!" IN 1492, when tidings of Christopher Columbus' great discovery flamed through Spain, these words were on every tongue. Adventurous hearts beat faster. Bold cavaliers crowded the cobbled streets of seacoast towns, eager to be off upon the high seas in the first caravels. At the court of Seville, courtiers clamored for audience with King Ferdinand and Queen Isabella to obtain Royal Licenses for expeditions to the Indies. Excitement came to the huts of the humble and to the palaces of the great.

The time was opportune. The infidel Moors, after eight centuries of merciless warfare, had been vanquished at last. Granada was taken. What now? Must these heroic soldiers, bred on the dangers of internal strife, sheathe their bloodstained swords and be content with ordinary life and commonplace pursuits? Never! The youth of Spain was attuned to restlessness, to violence, to valiant exploit. Another crusade was the answer, a crusade to conquer the fabulous lands found by the great Admiral Columbus. Priests hailed it as a crusade to spread the true religion among the pagans. Courtiers called it a crusade to extend the empire of Spain. A few forthright men, without dissembling, spoke of it as a crusade for riches.

A conglomeration of viewpoints and desires — a conglomeration of men. Rich and poor, nobleman and commoner, priest and criminal — lawyers, notaries, physicians and astrologers — these were the men who swarmed to Spanish ships to set sail for the distant Indies. Men easily inflamed for one cause or another. Men whom war had made greedy and cruel, but also daring and romantic. Men hardened to the physical sufferings of others and themselves, as well. Scornful of pain and peril.

It is doubtful if men bred otherwise and less inured to life's dangers could have even survived the rigors of existence in the new land. While we cannot approve the methods of Spanish conquest, we are forced to admire the fortitude of the conquistadors.

Next to Columbus himself, perhaps, the man who most merits esteem is Vasco Núñez de Balboa. Compared with other captains of his time, his was a rare humanity. Unusually wise as a leader of turbulent men, he was a man of deep loyalties and steadfast convictions — a man whose character was ennobled by achievement, sobered by responsibility, and mellowed by adversity.

He built a settlement in the wilderness of Panama where, after four centuries, there are regions still unexplored by white men. Indeed, recent expeditions, attempting to follow Balboa's famous route to the Pacific, have had to turn back because of insurmountable difficulties. It speaks well for the indomitable courage of the Spaniards of the sixteenth century that modern "progress" has been able to affect but lightly the conditions and modes of life in the Darien interior. The natives who survive still retain former customs. Reports of walled cities still circulate. White Indians with golden hair have been seen occasionally, but never often and only by the fearless who dare penetrate the unknown. Gold is still there in vast stores, for the impatient Spaniards but skimmed the surface.

In this book, the authors have attempted to recapture the reckless spirit of the times, to give the reader a vivid and fast-moving account of the greatest "gold rush" of all. The main objective of this biography, however, is of course to give an insight into the character of Vasco Núñez de Balboa. Balboa — to arouse a better understanding of him — has been treated subjectively. Thus we have in this volume recorded thoughts and emotions built up from facts, as we have ascertained them. Also, we have brought to light new evidence to show the pacific and gallant character of the man.

Although Balboa's life has been dramatized by the authors, the facts have in no way been distorted, nor has there been any attempt to follow a story pattern at the expense of truth. What is presented has been secured at considerable cost of time and effort from the known and little-known sources available in English, French, Spanish and Italian.

Here, probably for the first time, young readers can trace the life of the great explorer and pacifist in more complete chronological order. More of Balboa's early life is included than in most volumes. The actual events preceding Enciso's expedition to Terra Firma which led to the discovery of the Pacific Ocean are related in full. These include young Balboa's adventurous experiences in coming to the New World aboard one of the two caravels of the honest and kindly Bachelor, Don Rodrigo de Bastidas and, later, his unfortunate tenure of the land in crime-ridden Isla Española.

The book has been written not only for the pleasure it may bring to the reader, but further to inform and educate him upon certain historical events and characters of interest to all Americans. For that reason, it is our hope that *Hero of Darien* will prove valuable also as a supplementary text book in many of our schools.

HERO OF DARIEN

CHAPTER I

VASCO NÚÑEZ KNOCKS AT A DOOR

DARKNESS WAS CLIMBING THE HILLS, STEP BY STEP, TO THE VILLAGE
when young Vasco Núñez de Balboa entered the wide flagged
court of the alcalde mayor, Don Gaspard de Vorales, and looked
about him.

Night had already come quickly to the valley lands, but here
at the high elevation of the village there was still light enough
to see by, light from mountain peaks catching the last flame
from the western sky and pouring it over the flat-roofed houses,
cobbled streets, and the thin high spire of the Church of the
Sacred Heart and its nearby monastery.

Vasco Núñez had ridden hard and far that day, and as he
moved toward the entrance he made a weary gesture of running his fingers through his hair — a thatch as red as the re-
flected sunset. Outside the gate he could hear his horse clanking at its bit. From the scullery, at the back of the house, came

I

the rattle of pewter and clay plates and the delicious odor of braised meat. Low voices sounded inside and laughter and hurrying feet. Somewhere a dog barked.

Fourteen hours on the road, most of it mountain trail. Here he was at last in a strange village, before a strange house to meet a man of whom he had only vaguely heard, to discuss a matter that seemed no less presumptuous. The man he wished to see was Rodrigo de Bastidas, the notary, who had come here from Triana, near Seville, and was at this moment paying his respects to Don Vorales. The two men would talk far into the night, no doubt, about the recent granting of the Royal License and the coming expedition to Terra Incognita.

Vasco Núñez stopped short near the door. Doubt was beating in his mind like a drum. Now that only a few minutes separated him from meeting the famous notary and stating his desire, he had, he felt, no taste to go on with it. He wondered how he had ever had the courage to start out upon such an errand. Why had he presumed to think that a place on the expedition would be made for him? He, Vasco Núñez de Balboa, soldier and adventurer, the son of a nobleman whose estates were burdened with growing debt and mounting taxes — what chance had he? Better blades and stronger hearts in Seville, he had heard. Thousands were volunteering for the service because of the late reports of Admiral Columbus concerning the great wealth in Terra Firma. Gold was there, and unbelievable treasure. Cities of mystery and glamour. Practically everybody in the land of Spain must want to go to such a country, Vasco thought despairingly, and inasmuch as Rodrigo de Bastidas had requisitioned only two ships, probably the members of the expedition had already been chosen.

So Vasco Núñez hesitated before the door. A night wind

had sprung up and the light was dimming. Along this side of the house shadows grew wider and darker. Through the latticed windows the beams from candles went exploring into the courtyard, fluttering like moths around the stone benches and in the gathering darkness.

It had grown quieter inside. Dinner was being served, probably, in the great room just off the kitchen. Hunger drew the thoughts of Vasco Núñez there. He could, without much mental effort, look within the room to the meat steaming upon the boards. He could see the great loaves of bread piled in stacks and the wine bottles standing there like sturdy soldiers. There would be fresh boiled vegetables, too, from the Don's garden, and a very luscious pudding with its rich sauces, spiced and sweet — and, of course, nuts and fruits.

Vasco Núñez sighed and swallowed heavily. No ordinary dinner this, but a feast. A feast to celebrate Señor Bastidas' good fortune in receiving the Royal License, and to mark, in ties of friendship and mutual regard, the glorious event of the coming voyage. The young man knew — as who did not — that the two Dons, Rodrigo de Bastidas and Gaspard de Vorales, were about to take leave of each other after a quarter century of being such true friends that their names were usually mentioned in the same breath. They lived far apart in the Spanish kingdom and met only on infrequent occasions, but letters passed so constantly between them that it required a special messenger to deliver them. There was exchange, too, of books and papers and sealed documents. No learned opinion in the land escaped their attention. No finding of science or law could elude their earnest study and comment.

When the great Genoese admiral, Christopher Columbus, sailed on his first fateful expedition to the Indies bravely west instead of east, in defiance of all the dictates of precedent and common sense, the two Dons had loudly applauded him in spite of scornful public sentiment.

Vasco Núñez de Balboa had heard that Vorales might even accompany this new expedition himself. Vasco Núñez considered this story unlikely. Vorales was one of the fattest men in the whole of Spain, over three hundred in weight and unsteady on his feet. In fact, Vasco Núñez had been told that the mere thought of physical movement was distasteful to Don Gaspard de Vorales, who believed that the exercise of wielding his pen was sufficient. The departure of Señor Bastidas, his closest correspondent, would be like tearing out his heart, but better to suffer that than that he himself should endure the hardships and misery of the voyage.

Suddenly, Vasco Núñez, standing there so forlornly in the shadows, decided to give up his mad idea of trying to reach the golden Indies. He was a rash fool, he told himself sadly, an overbold nobody. He could never match his wits nor his blade with those adventurous young gallants from Seville — courtiers, many of them, who had influence with the king himself. What recommendation had he? None. His people were of a lower order of nobility, to be sure, but of no distinction or wealth. No, there was no one to speak in his favor except his late liege lord, Don Pedro Puerto-carrero, Lord of Moguer. But Don Pedro was deaf and old now, shorn of his former authority, and neither a favorite at court nor of importance elsewhere.

Balboa turned back to his horse. But in the very act of retracing his steps, he hesitated again. He thought of his father, of the troubles deepening around him. Had he not promised to recoup the family fortunes in Terra Incognita, come what might? He had told his father that if he failed to win a place in the expedition of Don Bastidas he would turn to young

Diego Columbus, son of the great admiral, or to Señor Nicuesa who had but recently received a grant of land on the mainland of the Indies.

Vasco Núñez squared his shoulders and thrust up his chin. No harm, at least, in stating his errand. If Bastidas said no, he could be no worse off. Refusal could only strengthen his determination. He would go somehow. He must. So much depended on it. His own future and the welfare of his family back in the village of Xeres de los Caballeros. His thoughts dwelt in particular on his younger brother, Gonzalo, who looked up to him as an example of valor. He must be a true model for Gonzalo, a leader of bravery. He must send gold and jewels to Gonzalo, so that all in Spain might be impressed by his splendor. Yes, for his parents, for Gonzalo, for the name of Balboa, he must do it.

He raised a resolute hand and struck the knocker on the door. Then, remembering an old trick of a pompous army officer, he unsheathed his sword and beat out a loud metallic tattoo as a complement for the knocking.

It was a furious noise indeed — like that of an entire regiment arriving. Vasco stepped back, abashed at his own tumult.

Almost immediately the bolts rattled inside and sudden light burned his eyes. An old servant peered through the opening.

"What do you want?"

"A message for the friend of your master," cried Vasco Núñez in an authoritative voice. "Make haste, my good fellow, and conduct me to him."

"You mean Don Rodrigo de Bastidas?" mumbled the servant doubtfully.

"Aye."

The servant hesitated. "And whom shall I say — ?"

"Do not dally," commanded Balboa, breaking in boldly.

"Hurry, fellow. Make haste, I say!" He pushed through the door, almost upsetting the startled servant.

"Si, señor," he said quickly. "Follow me."

Vasco Núñez followed the stooping figure along the hallway. Courage was running in him now like quicksilver. His hopes soared. The ease with which he had entered surely was a good omen. Perhaps he might even be invited to dinner. Hunger mingled so with the excitement within him that he could not truly tell which was which.

He said: "I have no wish to disturb your master, my good fellow, but my business with Don Rodrigo de Bastidas is most important."

The servant swung his head to regard again the impressive height of the young man, the resolute shoulders, the fearless blue eyes, that flaming shock of red hair ruffling beneath his brimless cap.

"Is—is señor perhaps a courier of the king?"

Vasco Núñez coughed suddenly to cover the awkward moment. They went on. Turning abruptly to the right, the servant passed through a low archway and thence to a high-raftered room.

Four persons sitting around a table looked up, startled.

Vasco Núñez de Balboa came sharply to attention.

"This courier—" began the old man uncertainly.

"Your servant is mistaken," Vasco interrupted. "I have only a request to make. But it is one that cannot wait." He stepped forward. "With your permission, Señor Bastidas."

"Speak," said the notary curiously.

The fat jowls of Don Vorales quivered with indignation. He had a small loaf of bread in one hand and he broke it upon the board.

"By what right are you here?" he thundered.

"I am a swordsman of some distinction," said Vasco Núñez. "I am a soldier with service. By your leave, I should very much like to accompany you to Isla Española and Terra Firma."

"Your name?" asked the notary.

"Vasco Núñez de Balboa."

"A nobleman, of course?"

"Yes."

"A nobleman of sorts," sneered Don Vorales. "His impudence is appalling. He looks to me like a rough fellow."

"The rougher the better." His friend smiled. "We need strong men. He has the frame of a giant." His voice was approving. "I have had difficulty in Seville, securing men of the right sort. The city swarms with incompetents."

"I am no incompetent, of that I can assure you," declared Balboa staunchly. "I have served eight years as a soldier."

Don Bastidas rounded his lips. "So? You seem young to have — "

"I am twenty-five."

"Where did you get those fiery locks?"

"From my father," answered Vasco proudly.

Don Bastidas nodded kindly. "I have met your father, and admire him. He is a learned man. He has written a tract upon the subject of astrology. For myself, I do not believe in it. But I must confess that his eloquence nearly convinced me to a contrary view."

"I believe in astrology," broke in Don Vorales heavily. "I believe in it and all that it portends."

"I do not."

"State your premise," challenged the fat host, "and I will refute it."

"That I defy you."

Vasco Núñez was forgotten completely. He stood there a

long time while the two friends, in wordy combat, strove to break down each other's opinion. The other two men at the table paid no attention to anything but the matter of eating as much as possible. Vasco Núñez watched, smelling the appetizing odor of meat and the fragrance of the pudding.

Suddenly he felt faint and weak. Would they never stop? Had the good notary, Señor Rodrigo de Bastidas, decided to ignore him? Was he expected to go now? He opened his mouth to enquire when, unexpectedly, Don Vorales' eyes fell on him.

"Have you supped?" he demanded.

"No, señor."

"Well, what are you standing there for?" grumbled the big man. "You are discourteous. I knew it. If this food reproaches you, or if there is anything I have said, that is your privilege, of course."

Vasco Núñez smiled. He knew now that Vorales was brusque in order to hide his generosity. He was irritable in speech to conceal the softness of his heart. Hope came again to the weary young man who had ridden hard and far that day.

He advanced and took a place at the table. As he did so, Don Bastidas nodded to him and said:

"You'll do, of course. Consider yourself one of us, Vasco Núñez de Balboa. It may be of interest to you to know that I have already received a very good account of you from Don Pedro Puerto-carrero. He praises your swordsmanship highly, and yourself as well. I received his letter before I left Seville."

The blue eyes of Vasco Núñez shone. He swallowed carefully.

"It — it is settled then?"

"What? What's settled? Oh, that you are to go on the expedition. Of course. Of course. I just said so, did I not?"

He turned impatiently to his host. "I insist that it is incredible and childish to imagine that the arrangement of heavenly constellations can affect —"

"Eat, young man! Eat!" boomed Don Vorales. "You are not sailing this instant to the Indies. The gold will wait, but the stomach will not." He sent a great plate of meat clattering down the board to Vasco Núñez.

Vasco Núñez de Balboa took a deep contented breath and fell to.

His dream had come true. He was sailing to Isla Española. He was at last to realize his dearest wish — to follow the route of the great Admiral Columbus to the Indies.

CHAPTER II

FAREWELL TO SPAIN

THE TWO CARAVELS OF RODRIGO DE BASTIDAS WERE READY AT LAST to depart. It seemed to Vasco Núñez de Balboa, standing on the deck of one of them, that the ships tugged restlessly at the restricting anchors. He, too, was eager to be off, flying before that freshening October breeze.

Nevertheless, there was a hint of wistfulness in his blue eyes as he looked across the harbor to where the snow-white buildings of Cadiz rose steeply from the sea. This was farewell to Spain, his native land. Was it forever? Or would he some day return, laden with gold and pearls, master of his own ship? Imagining the scene of his return, his mind tingled pleasantly. Young brother Gonzalo would indeed admire him then. His mother would laugh and weep at the same time. His father would place a hand on his arm and say, his voice trembling with pride: "Vasco Núñez, you have added luster to the ancient name of Balboa."

He laughed exultantly, throwing his handsome head back to sniff the morning air. His thick hair blazed in the sunshine. Oh, it was good to be alive on such a day, with all the unknown world stretched out before one, beckoning and alluring! This autumn day in the year of our Lord 1500 was one that he would long remember.

"You do well to laugh, my friend," said a voice beside him. "Never was a wind more favorable for sailing. My uncle says it is a good omen for the voyage."

Balboa turned, his blue eyes friendly. The young man who had addressed him was a few years younger than himself. Dark and lithe, he was fully a head shorter. He wore a doublet and jerkin which, Vasco Núñez saw, were of good material but not elaborate. Around his slender waist was a metal girdle from which hung a dagger.

Vasco Núñez liked what he saw. The young cavalier's brown eyes met his with appealing frankness and his whole body bespoke vitality.

"I am Vasco Núñez de Balboa, lately in the service of Don Pedro Puerto-carrero, Lord of Moguer. You have heard of my late liege lord?" he asked shyly.

"I regret not," replied the other apologetically.

Vasco Núñez shrugged. "Few have. But I praise your honesty in admitting it. I do not like the smoothly politic."

"Nor I." He bowed. "I am Sebastian Bernalo. This is my first voyage. My uncle says that until I have my sea legs it is not likely to be pleasant for me on a rough sea." He grinned at Balboa.

"He meant to say — until you have your 'sea stomach,' no doubt," said Balboa. "Well, I have never been to sea before, either, but I don't think the water sickness will trouble me. I am strong." He flexed his muscles, liking the vigorous feel of them.

"So am I," nodded Sebastian, "but my uncle says that makes no difference — "

"Your uncle," interrupted Vasco Núñez. "Who is this uncle of yours?"

"Juan de la Cosa," said Sebastian Bernalo, grateful that finally he had been asked to speak the name.

"Juan de la Cosa!" Vasco Núñez looked with increased respect at the dark young man beside him. "Why, he — "

"He shares the command with Don Rodrigo de Bastidas. He is navigator of our two caravels."

"I know. I have been wanting to catch sight of him!" exclaimed Balboa excitedly. "Why, Juan de la Cosa piloted the *Santa María* on the famous voyage of Admiral Columbus!"

Sebastian Bernalo flushed, enjoying the aura that relationship to the famous navigator gave him.

"He is the brother my mother holds most dear," he said. "When Uncle Juan returned from that first great voyage of discovery, he brought us many gifts from the new land."

"Ah," sighed Balboa, "but you are fortunate indeed. Would that I had some famous kin." He winked at Sebastian. "Well, the only thing for me to do is to make a name myself."

Sebastian looked at him admiringly. "It would not surprise me," he said, "if you did so."

As he spoke there was renewed bustle and activity aboard ship. Someone bellowed orders. Mariners scurried to comply.

"Look!" shouted Sebastian above the tumult. "They are weighing anchor. We are putting forth to sea at last!"

He thumped Balboa on the back. Vasco Núñez responded with such an enthusiastic whacking that poor Sebastian nearly plunged overboard into the sparkling waters of the Cadiz harbor.

The unfurled sails swelled as they caught the breath of the wind. Slowly, with majesty, the two caravels moved out of the protected basin into the open ocean.

After waving and shouting to those on shore, the two young men fell silent; the hills behind the white city grew farther and farther away. In the distance, they could hear the farewell tolling of the church bells.

Sebastian gulped and said a little hoarsely: "My mother and my three sisters came down to see me off. I should have liked you to make their acquaintance. You would have thought my youngest sister, Dolores, particularly pretty."

"I have no doubt," said Balboa politely, but he was secretly glad that he had not had to endure the ordeal of an introduction to so many females. Women were dull, he felt, in comparison to the wonders of the Indies toward which they were now sailing.

"Did your uncle," he asked, "bring back any pearls from the Indies?"

Instead of answering his question, young Sebastian Bernalo turned on his heel and strode off down the deck. Vasco Núñez had a quick glimpse of his distorted face.

"Why, he weeps!" he said, astonished. "All of twenty, and he blubbers like a boy!" He had the soldier's disdain for tears, but, nevertheless, his own throat ached in sympathy for his new friend. It was, after all, a long and uncertain voyage to Terra Firma. Hardships, he knew, must lie ahead of them. Perhaps death by the strange arrows of some pagan inhabitant. Possibly the sea itself might prove hostile, or the winds contrary. The ocean was wide and very deep, Vasco Núñez knew.

These thoughts were disquieting. In order to banish them, he strolled into a group of cavaliers near by. Such was his stature and general appearance that immediately all eyes were upon him.

One of them, taller than the rest, eyed him challengingly.

"Ah, here is the young torch-head who has been currying the favor of Juan de la Cosa's nephew!" His black eyes blinked narrowly at Vasco Núñez. He had a wide, broad-nosed face which hinted a taint of Moorish blood.

"I curried no favor," replied Vasco Núñez heatedly. "It was Juan de la Cosa's nephew who first made conversation with me."

"Ah," said the other, smiling jeeringly, "perhaps he curried your favor, instead?"

"That I doubt," said Balboa.

"And I."

"I do not favor your doubts, sir."

"I do not favor the color of your hair."

"Then perhaps you will favor the point of my sword!"

Two weapons whipped out at once. The cavaliers shouted, immediately taking sides in the struggle.

It was soon apparent that Balboa was much the better swordsman. Great-framed as he was, nevertheless he possessed a catlike lightness on his feet that astonished his observers. Finally, with a quick twist, his taunter's sword clattered to the deck.

Vasco Núñez stood over his panting opponent.

"What say you now of my hair?" he asked.

"I favor it. Truly, I favor it!" gasped the young man with fright.

"And what think you? Do I curry favors from Juan de la Cosa's nephew?"

"Never. I swear it."

A tall man shouldered his way through the crowd of cavaliers and soldiers.

"Who speaks the name of Juan de la Cosa? What commotion is this?" His hand fell heavily on Balboa's shoulder. "What, brawling, with the caravel barely out of Cadiz?"

Vasco Núñez straightened, recognizing the tone of authority.

"I'm to blame, señor. I felt called upon to reply to an insult."

"It is Juan de la Cosa," murmured someone.

Juan de la Cosa frowned at Vasco Núñez. "You began it?"

"Aye."

There was an approving murmur around the group at this forthright admission.

The navigator turned to the defeated duelist.

"What is your name?"

"Andrés Garavito," replied the other with extreme courtesy. "And yours?" His eyes raked Balboa.

"Vasco Núñez de Balboa."

Juan de la Cosa drew his eyebrows out of line. "Ah, I suspected as much. You are the bold young man who stormed the house of Señor Bastidas' friend to obtain an interview, are you not?"

"Aye." Balboa dropped his head, abashed. His was a temper instantly hot, but soon cooled. He regretted the rash duel with Andrés Garavito, and only embarrassment in front of such a company prevented him from saying so.

"Dueling aboard this caravel is forbidden," said Juan de la Cosa. "When the Indies are reached, our company will have need of every man, and every man must be in good health. For this first offense, I will not proceed with the deserved punishment. However, enough! No more battling among comrades. Save your warlike vigor for infidel attackers, should there be any."

Thus Vasco Núñez met Juan de la Cosa, but not as he had hoped to meet him.

Downcast, he turned to Andrés Garavito.

"Will you be friends?" he asked.

Andrés Garavito stared, then smiled uncertainly.

"Aye, if you will." But he spoke diffidently.

Vasco Núñez looked at him warmly. It seemed to him that their shared disgrace should serve to grapple them together as close comrades. He readily forgave the recent affronts. Before the friendliness in his blue eyes, Andrés Garavito's resentment dissolved. After all, this red-haired young man was a commanding figure, and an expert swordsman. It might be more to his advantage to have him as friend than as enemy.

During the remainder of the voyage the two were much together, although Vasco Núñez really preferred the quieter company of young Sebastian Bernalo. Sebastian, being younger and less experienced in the ways of the world than Balboa, looked up to him, reminding him a little of the way Gonzalo looked up to him.

Such was the sunny disposition of Balboa that he made friends everywhere. His only enemies were not of his making, but resulted from jealousy of his general popularity.

As the days went by and seemed to number as many as the fish in the great Sea of Darkness on which they sailed, Balboa thought it strange that he had ever lived otherwise than aboard a gallant caravel. His life seemed suspended between the past which was Spain and the future which was Terra Firma. It was difficult sometimes to credit the existence of either one.

But Juan de la Cosa said one day that the ships were nearing land. He gave as evidence broken branches of trees in the water and the appearance now and then of land birds.

"He will surely pilot us safely to the shores of the Indies," Sebastian Bernalo declared loyally.

Vasco Núñez was standing with Sebastian and Andrés Garavito on the day that the cry came that sent leaping the pulses of every man on board.

"Land ho!"

The long awaited shout rolled through the ship. Another voice took it up. Then another and another, until it was one great blended shout of joy.

"Land ho!"

CHAPTER III

LAND HO!

I<small>T WAS A SMALL ISLAND FIRST SIGHTED BY THE EAGER EYES OF THOSE</small> aboard the two caravels, but so green and beautiful with tropical vegetation that it had been named Isla Verde.

"Behold, it is like an emerald!" exclaimed Sebastian, his dark eyes luminous with excitement.

"Aye, it is indeed beautiful!" agreed Balboa.

Everyone was impatient to set foot on land again after months aboard the rolling vessels. Sebastian, Vasco Núñez, and Andrés were among the first to go ashore. They armed themselves well in coats of mail and kept their halberds ready to hand. Juan de la Cosa warned that the inhabitants of this islet might resent the intrusion and prove unfriendly.

"Nevertheless," said Rodrigo de Bastidas, "no one is to attack these people, unless they first show themselves hostile."

"What bad fortune," grumbled Andrés Garavito, "that our leader is a cowardly notary."

"Not cowardly," said Balboa, "peace loving."

"One and the same. I had hoped to see a rousing battle with these brown-skinned pagans."

Don Rodrigo, passing, caught the last words. He stopped, frowning.

"The purpose of this expedition," he said, holding Andrés with a severe eye, "is to trade with the Indians and secure from them gold and pearls, a goodly proportion of which goes, as you know well, to our sovereigns, King Ferdinand and Queen Isabella."

"Aye, señor," replied Andrés, with a servility which he donned at will like a convenient cloak.

"Such trading will be made easier if lubricated with courtesy and kindness. This is not cowardice but wisdom. If attacked, we fight. If not, we trade in harmony."

"I understand," said Andrés, bowing elegantly. "I am in full accord."

However, no natives came forth to greet the Spaniards, either with peace offerings or with arrows. Don Rodrigo decided to send out scouting parties to see if the island were inhabited at all.

Sebastian and Vasco Núñez were immediate volunteers, for they were anxious to see the remainder of the island. They joined a party led by Juan de Ledesina, a good friend of Don Rodrigo and a notary, too. Andrés Garavito went off with some others led by one of the two crown officers who accompanied the expedition.

The verdure was lush and sometimes so impenetrable that a path through it had to be cut with swords. In places, sunlight filtered through but dimly, so that everything was veiled with an eerie mystery. Vasco Núñez was enchanted by the strangeness of it all, amazed by the numbers of bright-winged birds with their odd cries, and delighted with the gorgeous flowers blooming in profusion.

They traversed the entire island without encountering a single native, nor did they find any fresh water. The other parties had no better fortune.

Disappointed, Don Rodrigo gave orders to make sail again, and the two caravels set forth for the mainland of Terra Firma.

They landed at Capo de la Vela, the long stretching head-land, where Alonso de Ojeda, another Spanish explorer, had been less than a year before.

Here, for the first time, Balboa saw the natives of Terra Firma. He was pleasantly surprised at the appearance of these people, for he had somehow supposed they must be as back-ward physically as they were said to be morally. This was not true. Most of them were tall of stature, well-knit and exceed-ingly vigorous. With such primitive weapons as they had — the bow, the lance and the buckler — they were expert.

"Why, they are truly more handsome than many a Spaniard I have seen," admitted Balboa reluctantly. He was filled with admiration for their strong, bronzed bodies and thought it would be a fine thing if all these people might be converted to the Christian faith.

He spoke of this to Andrés Garavito, who laughed.

"Convert them? Too much trouble. I say, slay them all and colonize the country with true Christians, the Spaniards!"

This was, indeed, the general opinion among the soldiers and cavaliers whom centuries of fighting against the pagan Moors had made ruthless.

Vasco Núñez de Balboa, however, felt strangely sympathetic with these natives and was glad that Don Rodrigo insisted that they be courteously dealt with.

The Indians regarded the Spanish invaders as gods, and brought them gifts of all kinds, odd beads and ornaments made from the bones of fishes, small white and green stones strung into necklaces and the beautiful plumes of tropical birds.

But these things were not what the Spaniards sought.

Irritably, Andrés Garavito flung away a fishbone necklace which one of the native maids had shyly given him.

"What do I want with such things?" he demanded, as the girl's eyes widened in bewilderment. "Gold, that is what I have come across the sea for. Gold and pearls!"

Balboa picked up the discarded bone necklace and put it over his own head, nodding and smiling at the Indian maiden. Then he strode over to the group where Rodrigo de Bastidas and Juan de al Cosa were vainly trying to explain that they desired more precious things than these poor presents.

"Perhaps if we were to show them a gold nugget or a pearl, they would understand," he murmured to Sebastian who stood beside his gesticulating uncle.

Sebastian shot him an approving glance. "Of course, that is a fine idea. I will speak to my uncle."

Juan de la Cosa at once dispatched some men to the caravels to bring samples of pearls and of gold. This strategy secured some results. The Indians appeared genuinely surprised that the Spaniards desired to trade shining beads and magnificent lengths of colored cloths for anything so worthless as gold and pearls. They appeared to feel that they were getting much the better bargain and watched the delight of the Spaniards curiously.

The cacique or leader of the tribe made it clear that if they desired gold and pearls more of it was to be found further along the coast. He pointed toward the setting sun.

The two caravels, therefore, coasted westward until in March, 1501, they reached uncharted seas and the mouth of a river which they named the Magdalena. Here they traded again — this time more profitably — with the inhabitants on the shores, but they were threatened with shipwreck in the strong current of the river which nearly sent them aground. It was largely due to the sound discretion of that able seaman, Juan de la Cosa, that they were able to continue unharmed.

Continuing along the coast and trading with the hospitable Indians as they went, they found and named Port Zamba and Port Coronados. The latter was so named for the very good reason that the natives there wore crowns of metal sometimes decorated with pearls and other semiprecious stones. These they were quite willing to present to the greedy Spaniards in exchange for inexpensive trifles from across the sea.

Setting sail again, they passed the islands of San Bernardo, Baru and the Arenas, off the coast of Cartagena. Sighting Fuerte and uninhabited Torluga, the vessels touched at the port of Cenú and passed Point Caribana.

It was a significant day for all aboard the caravels of Rodrigo de Bastidas, and especially significant for Vasco Núñez de Balboa, when they entered the Gulf of Urabá.

Here they saw mountain peaks rising steeply from the water near the Darien shore.

Standing beside Sebastian on deck, Vasco Núñez drew a deep breath of admiration.

"Ah," he said, throwing back his shining head, "I favor this land. What adventure and mystery are here!" He pointed to the river freshening the gulf. "Who knows whence that stream comes? Perhaps from some fabulous city of gold."

"Perhaps." Sebastian nodded, enthralled.

"Some day I shall follow it to its source." Balboa waved toward the mountain spires. "What lies beyond those peaks? Perhaps the riches of Cathay or the golden palaces of Cipango — "

"My uncle says," interrupted Sebastian, "that Amerigo Vespucci, who sailed last year with Ojeda, believes that this is an entirely new world and not outlying lands of Asia as Admiral Columbus believes."

"A new world altogether!" Vasco Núñez savored the notion

and found it to his liking. "A new land! All to be explored, all to be discovered, all to be conquered — in the name of Spain!" He thumped Sebastian between the shoulder blades so hard that that young cavalier winced. "Well, I mean to find out whether or not such a thing is so. Aye, Sebastian, I mean to scale those peaks — some day."

Thus far, the expedition of Rodrigo de Bastidas had discovered one hundred and fifty leagues of new seacoast and, through peaceful trading, had amassed a great wealth of pearls and gold.

The natives of the village at the mouth of the river Darien were at first inclined to be warlike, but were soon won over. Don Rodrigo renamed the gulf, Gulfo Dulce, because the waters were sweet and fresh and the taste was gratifying to the thirsty Spaniards.

Making sail, they went on along the isthmus to Point Manzanilla, El Retrete and Nombre de Dios.

But suddenly, a fearful discovery was made. The ships were both leaking!

After a frantic investigation the verdict was brought in — and it was most unfavorable. Both hulls were riddled.

Juan de la Cosa shook his head gloomily. "It is that dreaded ship's worm which abounds in these torrid waters. The teredo navalis, it is called. I have heard something of its ravages."

Panic flamed through both caravels. In such perilous condition, how long could they remain afloat?

CHAPTER IV

AN EXCITING VOYAGE

THE TWO SHIPS LAY AT ANCHOR, BARELY A LEAGUE FROM SHORE. The first reports of the damage done to them by the deadly teredo navalis were confirmed first by the ships' carpenters and later by Juan de la Cosa himself. As a result, there were hurried consultations in the master's cabin and conjectures among the crew as to the probable fate of the expedition.

Somehow that day of misfortune dragged on. Pacing the deck as others were doing while awaiting orders from Bastidas, Balboa could not bring himself to share the general fear, or to doubt that presently everything would be all right. The sun had a reassuring brightness. The land they were about to leave rolled away toward the horizon hopefully. The sea was blue and smiling. Life, at that moment, seemed good to him. How could a man lose heart? It was as if Providence were putting signs of encouragement where every man could read — in the sunlight, on the white-crested combers of the Caribbean, and in the very wind that tugged with gentle insistence at the furled sails of the two caravels.

Toward the day's close, Sebastian Bernalo came aboard from the sister ship to announce that a decision had been reached. It was the master's decision that, perilous though it might be, they were to set sail immediately for Cadiz.

"Better to try that than to rot here," said Sebastian, shrugging. "My uncle says it is our only alternative."

Balboa nodded. "And neither ship is leaking very badly yet, is it?"

"No."

"When we reach colder waters in the north, the worms may cease their boring," Balboa suggested optimistically.

"Possibly."

Although Sebastian had brought word of the decision to start for Spain at once, no orders came for the sailing. As twilight winged into sudden darkness, Vasco Núñez thought it curious how quickly night came to this land. He could see the candles sputtering in the cook's galley and starlight falling through the rigging to the shadowy deck.

Young Sebastian Bernalo said he was sleepy. He was going to his bunk for two winks before his watch came the next hour. Ship's duty was required of everyone now, for many of the sailors must be in the hold constantly, working to prevent the water from rising and the cargo moldering in the damp.

As his friend went off, Balboa turned back to the rail. He wanted to see the land once more before they sailed, that mysterious Terra Incognita he had come so far to find and now was leaving. Incredible, all of it — beyond any conception he had had of it in Spain or on the long voyage hither across the sea. Even its realization, the sight and feel of it, during the past few months, had brought less of actuality than of unreality. It was still like something he had dreamed — yet, marvelously, to be dreamed again at the first opportunity.

Indeed, if worms had eaten every grain of wood in each ship's bottom, he, for one, would return without regret to these strange shores. Mystery was still here and the spell of it had cast a curious longing over him. He wanted to plunge deep into its great forests, follow its shining rivers, scale its highest peaks. Some day, perhaps, he might even lead his own expedi-

tion into these wilds. The dangerous life of the explorer allured him. Gold and treasure he wanted, of course, in common
with the rest of the world, but within him lay something
deeper than that. It was the urge to meet the challenge of the
unknown and the seemingly unattainable.

So, leaning against the rail, Vasco Núñez de Balboa looked
out across the intervening league of sea to the mainland.
Darker now, but more beautiful and fascinating than ever. Its
lines had merged into a half obscurity, yet one could still make
out the looming farallones guarding the curving shore line, and
trace the river of fresh water far inland. His searching eyes
could even make out how the jungle mounted in steps as it ran
west and south through regions no white man had yet set foot
upon.

Far up along the slope of a hill, a torch sent out its beacons
into the night.

"Indians," said Balboa to himself. "They make camp there.
Or perhaps they worship at a shrine like the one Sebastian and
I discovered at Coronados."

Thinking of this, he was oblivious of everything on deck.
The wind cooled his forehead. It was so quiet it seemed the
silence went on tiptoe. Occasionally the scent of the mainland
was borne to him, rich and full and mysterious.

From the caravel of Rodrigo de Bastidas, anchored a short
distance away, abruptly sounded the disturbing clangor of a
bell. The signal to make sail! A command rang out sharply
from his own ship and the sailors, sprawled about the decks,
rose sleepily and hurried to their posts.

Soon the ships were racing along on the homeward voyage
almost as if nothing had happened to alarm them. Up forward, a group of soldiers from Seville, happy at last to be
returning to their homes and families, were offering up prayers

of thankfulness to the Holy Virgin. Somewhere on the poop a voice was singing.

Balboa went about his work willingly but with a certain sadness. He would be glad to revisit his father and brother and offer them a large part of the gold and pearls that had been apportioned to him, but he could never remain in Spain now. He could not. Others, if they wished, might do so. In fact, he had heard many of them state that this primitive savage country was not to be endured by civilized man. No amount of treasure, they had sworn, could ever tempt them to come here again. But he, Vasco Núñez de Balboa, born a nobleman, had not the tastes of his class. The pomp and intrigues of court, the brittle pleasures of society, the monotony of routine life paled to insignificance when compared to the thrills of new adventures in an unexplored land.

The next day and the week following, he was too occupied to dwell overlong on these matters. The two caravels were leaking badly now. Gloom spread over the crew, for there was neither rest for them nor much hope of completing the voyage.

"We shall go to the bottom, taking our bright hopes with us," prophesied Andrés Garavito gloomily.

"We shall, of a surety," agreed Sebastian Bernalo, "unless we can put into some port for repairs."

"Did your uncle tell you that?" asked Balboa.

Sebastian looked sheepish. "No, but he hinted as much. There was foreboding on his face."

Vasco Núñez smiled at the younger boy. "And what of our good master, Rodrigo de Bastidas? Is he equally depressed?"

"He is a fool," Andrés Garavito broke in sullenly. "Unmindful of our predicament, I can assure you. One would think he had not a care in the world."

Vasco Núñez was startled at this information. Bastidas had

always been considerate of his men and was beloved of them. He had treated them all as his equals. He had been generous, as well, in dividing the treasure, apportioning to each man not only his legal share of the proceeds of the expedition but a great deal more besides.

"That is hard to believe of Rodrigo de Bastidas," said Vasco Núñez slowly.

"I have heard as much, too," admitted Sebastian reluctantly. "It is said he is more interested in learning the language of the Indians we are conveying back to Spain than he is in our own safety."

"Extraordinary."

"He is planning to present them all to King Ferdinand and Queen Isabella," said Andrés scornfully. "If I had my way we'd make slaves of them and put them into that foul leaky hold to do some work. Is not the life of one Christian worth more than the existence of a thousand barbarians?"

This was a theory ingrained in the Spaniards through centuries of fighting the pagan Moors. Now and again, Vasco Núñez was stirred with vague doubts concerning it, and he was not in favor of making slaves of the very natives who had befriended them.

His faith in Rodrigo de Bastidas was restored a short time later, when, after taking aboard wood and water at Jamaica, they pushed on toward Española, looking for a sheltered harbor where they might put in and make repairs.

A day out from Jamaica both ships sprang new leaks so frequently that terror seized the crews and Bastidas himself was forced to labor side by side with his men. Canvas sails were cut in strips to calk the holes. Pitch was boiling constantly in huge caldrons in the cook's galley. Because of this, food was served cold and meat had to be eaten raw. One night Balboa saw six men fall from exhaustion. Three Indians died from the unaccustomed work. A demented sailor leaped overboard and perished.

Grateful was Vasco Núñez then for his tremendous physique and the great energy that had been given him. Day and night he did the work of three men. At last, however, on a certain cloudy morning he stumbled up out of the hold, knowing that even he could endure no more. The ships might sink, but he could not lift a hand to prevent it. There were hollows in his cheeks. His eyes strove to pierce the fog of weakness that made everything a blur.

Too weak to care much what happened, he lay down on deck.

It was then he heard a voice high in the rigging shouting: "Land! Land! Oh, mercy of God, the Isla Española!"

But the land sighted, they soon learned, was Contramaestre, a small islet just off the coast. Here the two caravels found shelter and were laboriously repaired. By now a strange heaviness lay upon all the air. There was a heat of a kind they had never before experienced, a high humidity and the complete absence of wind. So calm it was that the sea lay like glazier's uncooled glass, steam rising over its staring surface; the sky had lost its dome in thick murkiness.

Sailors manned the oars as they set out once more for home. Hot and weary they were, and desperate to lessen the leagues to Cadiz.

Soon, off to starboard, came a rumbling as of distant cannon. Then lightning flashes and quickly rising sea. Heaving waves were pounding the ships even before a breath of wind came out of the living wall of darkness ahead. But when the wind struck, it struck with fury.

The sailors left their oars and struggled with the sails. Vasco

Núñez heard the water crashing over the decks as he valiantly strove to snub a line to the mast. They were being driven back toward the island and presently reached the little cove again.

But there was no protection here from the wind or the rain, now falling in a great flood. Fearful that they might be dashed upon the shore, Juan de la Cosa gave orders to make one more attempt to go forward, this time in the lea of the mainland where the fierce gale might be broken.

Hours later, Vasco Núñez, still on deck with a few of the more hardy sailors, knew they could no longer ride the storm. Weakened by the incessant boring of the teredo navalis, the ship's hull was leaking again; nor was the other caravel in better plight. Already she was signaling to her sister vessel to go into the landlocked harbor just ahead, the port of Jaracua.

It seemed doubtful that they would ever make it safely. Both ships were filling with water and sinking fast. Fortunately, a lull in the wind permitted a safe entrance, but by now they were logged down, barely afloat, the ship's timbers shuddering as they sank lower and lower.

"The treasure!" The cry went up. "Save the treasure!"

Vasco Núñez struggled through a wild scene he was never to forget. Men trampled upon one another, carrying their belongings tightly clutched. Casks and barrels went overboard. Sailors threw themselves into the sea. On every side were cries for assistance.

Suddenly everyone was floundering in the water, fighting for holds on anything afloat. Some were swimming. The piteous shrieks of the Indian captives from Terra Incognita rang in his ears as he turned to look back at the two caravels disappearing below the tumbling waves.

CHAPTER V

EN ROUTE TO SANTO DOMINGO

SAFELY ASHORE WITH HIS OWN SHARE OF THE PRECIOUS CARGO, Vasco Núñez turned to aid others more exhausted than himself. Sebastian Bernalo staggered to the beach and gratefully released to him a small coffer he had rescued and fell gasping, barely out of reach of the thundering breakers. Andrés Garavito, loaded with arms and ammunition, wrenched away from the clutching hands of a soldier and swam to shore. Balboa recognized the soldier as Bartolomé Hurtado and immediately swam out and brought him to land. Then he went back again to aid a nearly drowned sailor. Time after time he went into the sea, and finally had the satisfaction of knowing that all were saved, except the poor Indians gone down with the doomed caravels.

The expedition was a sorry sight, weak and bedraggled, on a wild seacoast of Isla Española. But, at least, they were all alive and had saved most of the portable wealth. Little by little, as the violence of the storm abated, they began to take heart.

"Indeed, it might be worse," Vasco Núñez said sturdily.

Juan de la Cosa nodded. "Santo Domingo lies across the island."

Rodrigo de Bastidas brightened. "Is it far?"

"Aye, far enough to make the journey a difficult one. But not so far that brave men cannot reach it." He wrung the water from his doublet with determination.

"Then we can make it," said the notary positively, "for I have seen no braver men than these."

The country through which they must pass could not, however, furnish provisions for the entire expedition traveling over the same route, Juan de la Cosa said. Therefore, Rodrigo de Bastidas divided his men into three parties, two of them headed by Juan de la Cosa and himself. Balboa and Sebastian joined the band led by the latter's uncle, while Andrés Garavito reluctantly took his place in that of Rodrigo de Bastidas.

"Heaven knows where we'll end," he muttered to Balboa, when they bade each other farewell. "No doubt we shall stop to discuss philosophy or astrology with the natives along the way and forget all about reaching Santo Domingo."

Vasco Núñez laughed and thumped him between the shoulder blades.

"You must learn to look at things in a sunnier manner, Andrés. As for me, I look forward to exploring this part of Isla Española."

"You look forward to everything," sulked Andrés. Without further word, he turned to join his band.

Each group was provided with a coffer, stored with trinkets and trade goods for the Indians. By this means they hoped to secure provisions along the way. The gold and pearls were also distributed, but the main part was carried by Rodrigo de Bastidas.

The natives proved friendly and were quite willing to supply the shipwrecked Spaniards with food in exchange for a bright length of cloth or some shining trinket of little value. The expedition often spent the nights in the villages of hospitable Indians and Balboa, though feeling his superiority as a Christian and Spaniard, took pleasure in making friends with them and studying their curious ways. Sebastian, though a great admirer of Balboa, was, however, to diffident to follow him in this.

"They are queer," he said soberly, when Balboa laughingly exhibited a string of shells given him by an Indian maid. "I cannot feel at home with these people. Besides," he said loftily, "they are infidels — no better than the Moors."

"It is true that they are pagans," agreed Balboa, "but they have been very generous and hospitable, considering that we are as alien to them as they are to us."

"Aye."

"I wonder," he said, "were they to invade Spain if we would receive them as well."

"That is entirely another matter," protested Sebastian. "Vasco Núñez, you speak with the softness of a woman."

Balboa drew his brows together in mock anger. "I have dueled for less insult than that, Sebastian. I beg you to retract that speech."

"Then of course I do — for Bastidas has said there is to be no brawling on this journey. But I tell you truly that I — "

"Give over." Balboa placed his hand on the younger man's shoulder. "I have no wish to quarrel with you, Sebastian. We are friends. Would that we could remain here in this new land and go exploring together."

"Remain here? Are you mad?" Sebastian's brown eyes were dark with horror. "I would as soon stay in the depths of Hades and go exploring amid fire and brimstone!"

"Ah, Sebastian, I see a sickness gnaws at your vitals."

"A sickness? Why, I swear I have no sickness."

"But you have. I know the signs. A sickness for the sight of home — for the voices of your mother and your sisters." Balboa smiled understandingly. "I, too, felt the same misery when first I joined the service of the Lord of Moguer. But now my inter-

est in this strange country has taken lead over my longing to
return to Spain."

Sebastian strode away into the shadow as he always did when
moved, for fear that someone would see.

As Balboa looked after him, a voice spoke his name. He
looked up to find the soldier, Bartolomé Hurtado, approaching.

"Aye, I am here. Did you wish to speak with me?"

"I have come," said the other haltingly, "to thank you."

"To thank me? Indeed, you are welcome. But for what?"

"For saving my life," replied Hurtado simply. "Had you not
rescued me from the sea that fateful day of shipwreck, I should
surely have perished."

"I cannot be sure of that. Someone else would surely have
succored you."

"But you did, and I thank you for it."

"I accept your thanks," replied Balboa warmly, "with additional thanks."

"Some time," declared Bartolomé sincerely, "I shall find a
way to repay you. I swear it."

Not more than a few days' journey from Santo Domingo,
according to the calculations of Juan de la Cosa, they camped
for the night in a native village, trading as usual for supplies.

Hardly were they settled for the night when a clamor arose
on the outskirts of the village. Instantly awake, Vasco Núñez
stepped to the door of the native hut which a number of the
Spaniards had taken over. By now he had learned to recognize
some Indian words and as he listened the name Spaniard came
to him clearly. Did it mean that someone from Santo Domingo, hearing of their sad plight, had come to escort them to
the Spanish settlement?

But the commotion died away mysteriously and nothing further was heard. Juan de la Cosa questioned the Indian cacique

the next morning but received little information as to the cause of the previous night's disturbance. The cacique admitted that some Spaniards had passed that way but would not say from whence they came or whither they rode. He professed not to know.

"Did they know of our presence here?" demanded Juan de la Cosa.

The cacique would not say.

They pressed on for Santo Domingo more feverishly than ever, anxious to reach the settlement as soon as possible. But when they reached it, incredible news awaited them. Rodrigo de Bastidas, who had arrived a day ahead, had been thrown into prison.

"But surely Admiral Columbus wouldn't —"

"Admiral Columbus! It is not Columbus who governs here now," they were informed. "He was superseded by Francisco de Bobadilla who sent him back to Spain in chains."

"In chains! The Admiral Columbus!" gasped Balboa, amazed that such a thing could be. "Why, he is the discoverer of these very lands."

"True, but not as successful an administrator as navigator," said his informant, "although truly not bad enough to deserve his cruel treatment." The man went on, lowering his voice furtively, "It is said that back in Spain he has been released and the king and queen have disclaimed all responsibility for the act."

"Ah, I am glad to hear that," said Balboa, relieved that his hero had been freed. "But what of Rodrigo de Bastidas? Why has Bobadilla imprisoned such a good man? For what cause?"

Bastidas was accused, Balboa learned, of carrying on illicit trade with the Indians. An alarmist report had reached the governor that a band of adventurers, divided into three parties, was marching through the country with coffers of gold.

"But not for gain, that I know well," protested Balboa. "The only traffic with the natives was for the purpose of securing food and guides for the journey hither."

This was indeed true, but it was a difficult task to prove it to the suspicious Bobadilla, jealous of his position and overbearing in his attitude toward those he governed.

"It is unfair!" exclaimed Balboa, careless of being overheard. "It is unjust! Why Rodrigo de Bastidas, castaway as he is with his two gallant caravels lost, should be the object of compassion, not persecution."

"Hush," said one of the cavaliers warningly. "Do you want to join him in prison? Our sympathy can avail little. We had best see to the saving of our own skins."

"A coward's path, that!" Balboa said scornfully.

Nevertheless, he did not again speak in public in defense of his former master, but only to a few trusted comrades. He was determined to do something about the sorry plight of the notary of Triana.

CHAPTER VI

SANTO DOMINGO — CITY OF INTRIGUE

OTHER LOYAL FOLLOWERS OF RODRIGO DE BASTIDAS WERE EMBITtered by the outrageous conduct of Bobadilla, the highhanded Governor of Española. Led by the headstrong Vasco Núñez de Balboa they formed a plan to rescue the notary from prison immediately.

Vasco Núñez confided the plot to Bartolomé Hurtado, hoping to enlist him.

"We will attack in force and overpower the guards. Then we will convey our commander to a ship bound for Spain. Everything is in readiness."

Hurtado was silent, then said slowly: "There is a better way."

"A better way than that? What, pray?"

"Do nothing."

Balboa regarded his new friend in amazement. His words sounded utterly foolish, to say the least. To stand by and permit Bastidas to suffer such indignities was the part of craven men, not loyal and true comrades. The governor certainly had exceeded his authority in this case, and when the news of the rescue came to the attention of King Ferdinand there would be no reprisals nor arrests. Rodrigo de Bastidas had a royal warrant. He had powerful friends in court who would resent what the governor had done.

" 'Tis Bobadilla and not the good Bastidas who should be put in irons!" Vasco Núñez declared hotly.

"True," admitted Bartolomé.

"Then I fail to see — "

"If you'll come with me," Bartolomé said earnestly, "I'll explain everything. With your own eyes you shall see what kind of a man this Bobadilla is. His handiwork is traceable in every street and corner of this town."

From the quays and wharf fronting the beautiful harbor, the two young men went arm in arm up the one cobbled street and into the huge plaza or business section of Santo Domingo. The harbor had smacked of the sea and all the smells of cargo and ships, so familiar to them. But here, in the center of the town, there was an atmosphere entirely different. Taverns on every hand with roistering crowds and blasphemous men. Drunkenness, brawling and cruelty. License unchecked by civil authorities. No rule, no law, no order of any kind. The governor had closed his eyes to the horrible conditions in order that he might exact tribute in gold.

To Balboa, stumbling along, wide-eyed, there came remembrance of the words of the great Admiral Christopher Columbus whom this same Bobadilla had sent back to Spain in chains.

"I swear that numbers of men have gone to the Indies who did not deserve water from God or man."

Proceeding around the public square, the two comrades came to the Casas Reales, a group of buildings distinguished from the others by a well-kept appearance and an air of opulence. No expense had been spared to make the principal building, the governor's residence, imposing. To some extent this was also true, Vasco saw, of the arsenal and cabildo, the latter housing the municipal offices.

They stopped before one of the buildings. "What is that?" asked Balboa, pointing to it.

"That? Why, that is the casa de la fundacion — the house of gold."

"Gold!"

"Aye, the gold of all the Indies comes here, sooner or later, to be divided. Or perhaps, to speak more accurately, I should say to be weighed, melted and appraised by representatives of the government. The royal one-fifth is set aside for the crown and shipped to our worthy sovereign, may God bless and keep him."

"I had heard of that." Balboa nodded.

"What you have not heard," Bartolomé continued, raising his eyebrows, "is the manner of the weighing and the notorious unfairness of the scales. Although the crown probably receives just portion, it is common knowledge that the original owner of the gold never does — unless he be a friend of the governor. Aye, you can be sure that some very curious things are going on here."

Balboa blinked his eyes. "For example?"

"Well, there was the case of my friend, Don Alberto Recendez, who returned to Santo Domingo from Terra Firma not long ago aboard one of the caravels of Alonso de Ojeda. His share of the gold gathered along the strange shores they touched upon, though not considerable, was still sufficient to provide him with the necessities and luxuries of life for some time to come. Ojeda had presented it to him after the royal fifth had been subtracted here at the casa de la fundacion."

Bartolomé Hurtado paused to scowl in the direction of the building he had just named. Following his gaze, Balboa saw two guards in heavy armor standing at its entrance. Men entered or departed hurriedly — always hurriedly — and their expressions were alternately greedy or despairing. Sometimes their faces were inflamed with fury, their hands clenched and their lips compressed.

One poor fellow, wearing little more than a breechclout and a ragged doublet, stepped forth weeping. One of the guards pricked him unsympathetically with the point of his halberd to speed him on his way.

"He has been robbed," Hurtado said grimly, "just as my friend Alberto was."

Balboa stared. "Robbed by whom?"

"The country abounds in thieves," Hurtado said. "They were allowed to come here from the Spanish prisons, having been granted immunity if they would settle the colony."

"Aye, I have heard that King Ferdinand is giving criminals their liberty, passage and free lands to cultivate, in order to attract people to the Indies."

"But now they are overrunning the island, stealing and plundering from honest men," went on Bartolomé Hurtado.

Balboa watched the man whom his friend declared had been robbed. Pity welled up in him. The man's spirit was broken and he looked very poor indeed. When he had disappeared into a crowd a short way down the street, there came suddenly a new distraction.

Approaching along the plaza, making a great clanking noise, were a full score of strange persons of all ages. Big swarthy men, for the most part, but here and there a woman or a child. All of them natives of the new land, Balboa perceived, and in bondage, every one. They were chained to each other at the ankles, and the heavy chain scraped, thumped, and rattled over the flagstones. Behind and around them strode guards carrying long whips which they cracked over the heads of the prisoners. When a native lagged or stumbled, the whips bit mercilessly into a bare shoulder or other part of the body, raising huge welts.

Vasco Núñez de Balboa had not served as a soldier in Spain without witnessing acts of cruelty before, but never anything which could compare with this. He stood ashamed of his countrymen. He trembled with indignation that the civil authorities should permit it. Again Columbus' words of condemnation rang in his mind. Such evils had never been sanctioned by the great admiral during his administration, for he had striven to remedy them.

However, affairs in Santo Domingo had been taken over by a lawless clique, many of whom were recruited from former Spanish convicts. Thousands of unfortunate Indians such as these, inhabitants of Española, were brought into the settlement, Hurtado said, for work in the towns and outlying estates or haciendas. Here they toiled as slaves, without pay, and were often so sorely mistreated by their masters that they died by the hundreds.

Balboa decided that if he should ever become a landowner himself, he would treat his slaves kindly. After all, they were human like himself. Surely it was no fault of their own that they were without knowledge of the Christian faith. Priests, he had heard, had already succeeded in converting many of them. They did not denounce Christianity in the pagan manner of the Moors, but were willing converts. Why, then, should they be thus persecuted?

The miserable cavalcade went past while he was pondering these things. Hurtado stood at his side, still scowling, and presently he remembered that he had not finished his story about Don Alberto.

"I met my friend only this morning," he resumed. "I found him in great despair and penniless. His gold had been stolen the same day Admiral Columbus was arrested by Bobadilla and thrown into prison. As the thief was known to him, he applied for a hearing of the case in the courts, hiring a lawyer to prosecute the guilty one."

"Ah, of course," approved Balboa, "that was the thing to do."

"One would naturally believe so, but Bobadilla's own judge exonerated the thief, although all the evidence clearly showed that the defendant, a former convict, was guilty."

"But I fail to understand," puzzled Balboa, "how that could be."

"When the thief stole the gold he went immediately to the casa de la fundacion and declared it. It was then assayed and registered as having come from a certain mine owned by the thief in a remote part of Española. Of course, the mine existed only in the thief's mind. Yet the gold was remelted and its registry gave the criminal his claim to it. This false claim was, in the eyes of the law, apparently a stronger one than any my friend could present in court."

"How unjust!" exclaimed Balboa.

"The more times the gold can be brought into the casa de la fundacion by thieves," explained Hurtado, "the more revenue there is for Bobadilla and his black crew." He drew Balboa aside, lowering his voice as he did so. "Robbing and thieving are actually encouraged, so guard your treasure well."

"Be assured I will!" Balboa's face was grim.

"Now you understand why I do not favor the rescue by force of our good friend, Rodrigo de Bastidas."

"But I do not understand! All the more reason to outwit the villainous — "

"I will tell you. Conditions here will not improve under Bobadilla. You have seen with your own eyes how terrible they are. Columbus has been sent back in chains. Bastidas will follow him. Our gracious sovereigns know that finer men than these two never breathed upon the soil of Española. They will be exceedingly wroth and then — "

"I see," said Balboa eagerly. "Then they will send out a new governor to Santo Domingo."

"Exactly. So let us bide our time. Sometimes patience weaves a better pattern than a sword."

"I agree. But meanwhile — what shall we do? We are for the moment stranded in Española."

Hurtado considered. "We might try to buy our passage back to Spain, but we should exhaust our treasure doing so."

"Perhaps we might win a place on some exploring expedition," suggested Vasco Núñez, excitement shining in his blue eyes.

Hurtado shook his head. "That I doubt. No, the best thing for us to do is to become farmers. We can operate our own haciendas outside the town. There is much fertile land for growing crops and a great demand for them, I have heard."

Balboa shook his head doubtfully. "I am not well acquainted with tilling the soil. In fact, I know nothing of it. I have been trained as a soldier, not a farmer. Besides, how shall we go about securing the land?"

"Ah, that is easy!" Hurtado clapped him on the shoulder. "One can easily secure a concession from the authorities, for the scarcity of food is becoming a serious problem. The casaba plant, my friend Don Alberto told me, supplies the flour for most of the bread eaten here. Raising it is bound to be profitable."

As Balboa still hesitated, Hurtado turned and pointed toward the casa de la fundacion.

"So long as that place is in charge of Bobadilla, we can expect no just division of any gold we might gather, either in Española or on Terra Firma. But two young noblemen might do well conducting their own estates in the country, eh?"

Balboa laughed, tossing his bright head in the sun. After all, why not? It was worth a try. The idea was beginning to appeal to him. By farming he might earn enough castellanos to finance his own expedition to ever-alluring Terra Firma.

"Very well," he said heartily, "we shall lay our plans. Let us go about the town in search of information and guidance."

Arm in arm, the two vigorous young cavaliers swaggered off, elbowing their way through the jostling crowds.

CHAPTER VII

THE PLANTATION AT SALVATIERRE

BOTH BALBOA AND HURTADO WERE SOON ON THE LAND, THEIR plantations near the seacoast town of Salvatierre adjoining each other. Here, fired by youthful enthusiasm, they proceeded upon their new careers.

By late March, 1502, the two friends, at considerable expense, had put up their haciendas. Land had been cleared of jungle trees and vines. Casaba plants, grapes and native sugar cane were beginning to grow in the fertile soil so laboriously worked with the crude implements they had contrived for the purpose. Then, too, there was a vegetable garden sprouting costly Spanish seeds, garlic, onions, and green peppers. There were orderly beds of spinach and lettuce and long full rows of peas and beans.

In the beginning, they hired very little of the work done for the very good reason that they had not enough castellanos to pay for it. Their capital was limited, especially Balboa's, who had sent the greater part of his proceeds of the Bastidas expedition to recoup the family fortunes in Spain.

At first it was fun to chop down the strange-foliaged trees and cultivate the ground. Balboa experienced a certain satisfaction, too, in resting upon the verandah after a hard day, the ocean breeze cooling his heated skin and his mind dreaming without purpose. There was the contentment of achieving something each day. Another acre cleared, another plot seeded.

Sometimes in the evenings Bartolomé brought his guitar and

44

with his skillful fingers created the strains of romantic Castillian music or the wild plaintive songs of the gypsies.

On rare occasions they received letters from Spain. Sebastian Bernalo wrote to say that he had arrived safely in Cadiz. At Seville, he said, they were clamoring for the return of the oppressive Bobadilla. Columbus had been exonerated by their majesties and Rodrigo de Bastidas was now a free man and a rich one, too, as the result of his expedition. Moreover, the notary had been granted an annual revenue for the duration of his life — this to be derived from the province of Urabá which he had discovered. To his uncle, Juan de la Cosa, a like pension was assigned and he had been appointed Alguazil Mayor. His uncle could hardly wait to return to Terra Firma. It was Sebastian's private opinion that his renowned relative had been enchanted by some strange potion or other — hence his eagerness to return. As for himself, he was content to spend the rest of his days in Spain. Everything desired for a man's happiness was here. His mother, his sisters — the handwriting wavered, then flowed on strongly — the girl he was to marry.

Balboa clapped his knee, laughing, to see these words.

"That sly fox — I knew something stronger than the love of parents or sisters drew him back. Young Sebastian was lovesick, not homesick — but perhaps both."

Bartolomé Hurtado nodded, smiling. "Once or twice I suspected as much. He was so oblivious to the charm of native maidens."

"So did I. But when I asked him, he denied it. He was shy, Sebastian. Still, we were friends. He could have trusted me with his sweet secret."

He returned to the letter, his brows drawn together in a frown of concentration. There was no more about Sebastian's betrothed, no name, no description, no details. As if embarrassed by what he had already written, young Bernalo hurried on to more impersonal news. It was rumored that Admiral Columbus had asked that his son be sent to Isla Española to replace the governor. But the Bishop of Burgos, Juan Rodrigo de Fonseca, who was in almost complete charge of affairs in the Indies and close to King Ferdinand, opposed the idea. He objected on the grounds that there were others better qualified for such an exacting post.

"Fonseca is an enemy of Columbus," said Hurtado. "He is a villainous man, that one. I have no doubt that behind the king's back, he encouraged Bobadilla's treatment of the good Admiral Columbus."

"Aye, so they say." Balboa smiled at his friend. "I hope I shall never incur his displeasure. But that's unlikely, for it is said he spends his venom only on the great."

"And farmers," said Hurtado, "rarely achieve renown." He sighed. "Sometimes I long to go adventuring again over the sea to Terra Firma."

"And I," said Balboa. "But this life is better than returning to Spain."

Indeed, although Vasco Núñez de Balboa might read with intense interest all that was contained in the infrequent letters that came from his native country, from his father or brother Gonzalo, from his former liege lord, Don Pedro Puerto-carrero, and finally, one from Rodrigo de Bastidas himself — he still had no desire to return. The land of his adoption he had loved at first sight and his attachment to it grew as each day passed. Even now, struggling as he was to stem the ceaseless sprawling of the jungle over his land, and enduring hardships far from pleasant, he was glad of his choice.

One thing alone stood in the way of his complete happiness.

It seemed not quite fair that he and Bartolomé Hurtado should work so hard for so little, when other owners of haciendas along the seacoast did practically nothing. They, too, had started humbly and with little money. Yet now the stroke of an axe was never impelled by their arms. There were no calluses on their soft palms, no aches in their backs at the day's end. No, they were truly gentlemen of leisure. Roistering, gambling, drinking from dawn to dark. Spending most of their time in Santo Domingo, mingling with the elect.

Why? Balboa knew well the answer. They had slaves. Not purchased slaves, though slaves were often bought and sold in the markets of Santo Domingo, but slaves taken by force from native villages. Indeed, this ruthless taking of slaves had become a business more profitable than farming or even the hunting of gold. And if one farmed with the aid of slaves, how quickly the land could be cleared and the crops put in. Often Balboa would view his few humble acres with a sickening despair, knowing that not far away were haciendas that were vast by comparison. Magically, they appeared to grow larger overnight.

At the end of the fourth year both he and Bartolomé Hurtado could see that they were hopelessly outdistanced. The day-after-day drudgery had become monotonous. They had no time for leisure. Hunters went by, riding after game. They walked. Often a nearby plantation owner added to the excitement of living by going away into the interior for gold. He and Hurtado never went. They dared not. If they did the jungle would creep back and reclaim their hard-won fields and straggling garden plots.

Among the visitors who came frequently to visit them was one Juan de Valdivia, a nobleman. Valdivia lived like a prince.

He had an estate near Santo Domingo, a home in town and money invested in many profitable enterprises. He was especially fond of Vasco Núñez de Balboa.

"Your honesty and patience are truly a glowing example in these times," he told him once. "When I think of you, I no longer despair for the world of men. Nevertheless, I know you are a very foolish young man."

Balboa's pleased smile disappeared. "Foolish? Why?"

"You should take advantage of the times. If you kept slaves, you would be wealthy in a very short time. This way —" He shrugged.

"But the slaves are treated most cruelly," Balboa reminded him. "As a result, unused to such hard and continuous toil, they die like flies."

"But that need not be. With kind masters such as you would be —"

"Aye," Hurtado agreed, "slaves would not be made to suffer under us. We would feed them well and treat them kindly."

"That is true." Balboa nodded. "They would not be mistreated."

Having made his point, Valdivia a few days later offered them a loan on convenient terms for the purchase of a few slaves. Loath at first to accept the offer, Balboa finally agreed. He and Hurtado made a trip into the hills to a camp where natives were being brought in to be trained for the hard manual labor at the mines and farms and on the roads then under construction.

They had no difficulty in selecting twenty men they thought would be suitable and returned at once to their own haciendas.

True to their word, they were kind to these natives. The slaves were well housed, well fed and made to work only a reasonable number of hours. Balboa mingled with his own men as much as possible, learning their language and seeking their confidence. Aside from his genuine sympathy with the natives, he felt that sometime his knowledge of them might be useful. He didn't intend to remain a farmer all his life. Some day he hoped to make a long journey into the interior, bartering for gold and pearls just as Bastidas had done.

Though he made many plans for such an expedition, certain things happened in quick succession to delay him. Three of his slaves escaped one night and when he went to search for them, his plantation was visited by a gang of thieves from Santo Domingo and most of his crops stolen. Four more of his slaves had disappeared, as well. Whether they had run away or been taken with the other plunder, he did not know. To make matters worse, he could not find the original three who had escaped. Nor could Hurtado or anyone else give him a description of the white men who had stolen his crops. His debt to Valdivia worried him. Without income, how could he pay his benefactor the first year's installment on the loan?

Desperate, he decided to leave his farm for a time and go far into the wilderness in search of gold. One successful expedition would enable him to pay all his debts and start over again. Valdivia approved the idea and gave him a letter to certain merchants in Santo Domingo highly recommending him, for he would need credit for supplies of food for the trip. He would need trinkets, cloth and wearing apparel for barter with the Indians. Valdivia had always been very fair in his dealings with Balboa, but the merchants of Santo Domingo, greedy for profit, charged him triple price for everything he purchased. Although Balboa realized that he could do nothing about it, their unfairness rankled in his mind. However, this was soon forgotten in the joy he experienced traveling with his three native helpers into the wilderness of the interior.

All the old enthusiasm he had known while on the expedition with Rodrigo de Bastidas came back to him. He loved to plunge deep into the jungle and feel its mystery all about him, its brightly plumaged birds, its gorgeous flowers, its strange insects and reptiles. He liked to sit at night with the silence droning in his ears and his campfire sending out light that dropped like a necklace of gold among the palms. Sometimes, when the huge stems of the trees were black in the starlight, he would stand silent and dreamy eyed watching the hordes of fireflies sparkling in the foliage or playing hide-and-seek among the clustering vines.

The outdoors and especially the unknown worked a spell over him that he seemed almost powerless to resist. Occasionally, too, he thrilled to the danger of attack from unfriendly Indians. More than once from some leafy and hidden ambuscade, arrows would come whistling past him. The quickly diminishing tribes of Española, pressed by slave hunters and ruthless gold traders, still fought back at times.

Balboa's efforts in disposing of his high-priced merchandise unfortunately was not always successful nor profitable. Unlike the merchants of Santo Domingo he couldn't, with a clear conscience, defraud anyone, even an infidel. And gold was not nearly so plentiful as it had been in Terra Firma. Slave hunting was the one big industry here and it paid huge dividends.

Hounds were needed on expeditions like this. The dogs were invaluable both as fighters and as trackers. After the second or third expedition, Balboa began to use them more and more, training them for incredible feats of tracking through the wilderness to little-known Indian camps back in the hills.

One of the dogs he purchased in Santo Domingo was Leoncico, a sensitive-nosed, long-eared little puppy sired by the famous Beçerrico, a remarkable fighter and Indian hunter. The

fame of Beçerrico had spread all over Española and when Vasco
Núñez purchased the puppy from its owner, Juan Ponce de
Leon, he was determined to make an even greater fighter and
hunter out of the son. In this he succeeded.

But in all his other ventures he failed. He was now more
deeply in debt than ever. Merchants in Santo Domingo were
clamoring for their money. At last there came a time when he
had to hide from them, for a man sued for debt and losing his
case was liable to prison. And now a new law had been passed,
forbidding any debtor to leave Española until his obligations
had all been met.

Living from hand to mouth, hunted by process servers and
pettifoggers, Balboa's last two years at Santo Domingo were
almost unendurable. Had it not been for certain true friends
such as Valdivia and Hurtado, he might have been entirely
hopeless.

Often, feeling despair creep over him, he thought longingly
of Terra Firma, that land of golden promise and scene of his
earlier adventures.

His creditors were becoming more demanding. It would
soon be impossible to stave them off longer. Somehow, in some
way not yet revealed to him, he must make his way to Terra
Firma and there start his life afresh.

CHAPTER VIII

THE STOWAWAY

As the two vessels of his fleet put out to sea, señor martin Fernández de Enciso gave strict orders to search the holds and rigging carefully.

"I want no stowaway debtors aboard," he said sternly.

His eyes went to the armed caravel which followed and which had orders to take any desperate evaders of debt back to Santo Domingo. True, the governor had ordered constables to watch the ships that morning while the last barrels of provisions were being placed on board, but Señor Enciso was a thorough man, with a just loathing for those who sought to evade the law by which he made such a pleasant living.

However, Enciso soon had the satisfaction of signaling the armed caravel that all was as it should be, and the convoy turned about and headed back again to shore.

It was a very warm day, despite the breeze billowing the sails so encouragingly. The elaborate doublet and jerkin, which he wore, had been chosen more for display than comfort, and Enciso's face was even more florid than usual. Nevertheless, he was in good humor. Alonso de Ojeda had succeeded in making him believe that his secure and profitable years in Santo Domingo had in reality been unbearably dull. Only the brave and adventuresome could hope to attain the heights, said Ojeda. If Señor Enciso would invest his money in the glorious enterprise of founding a new colony in Terra Firma, he would be assured of the impressive office of alcalde mayor. The ambitious Enciso had been unable to resist the tempting offer.

Martín Fernández de Enciso felt sure at this moment that he could not have made a better investment. He congratulated himself mentally, a look of smug self-esteem overspreading his countenance. Not only was the future alluring, the present smiled. His ships were the best. His crew of one hundred and fifty had been carefully chosen. His provisions were ample, the equipment superior. He beamed upon the barrels of salt pork which had had to be placed on deck since the holds were overflowing. Yes, his hard-earned castellanos had been well spent. The rest was simple — he had merely to deliver the caravels and their cargo to Alonso de Ojeda — no doubt well established by now somewhere along the shores of the Gulf of Urabá — and then take over his high office.

Enciso's well-fleshed fingers toyed with the ornate gold chain depending from his neck. Contentedly, he watched Española shrink to a tiny dot on the horizon and rejoiced that he was many leagues of water nearer the realization of his ambitions.

Suddenly an odd sound invaded his ears. He turned his head, eyes casually scouring the nearby surroundings. It came again. Queer. It was like the noise of metal ringing against wood. A sturdy thumping, it was, and seemed to issue from one of those hogsheads yonder. But impossible! They were all filled with pork.

Not all, Señor Enciso! For even as he reassured himself, the top of one of the casks shot from its position. What seemed at first a flame to Enciso's dilated eyes became the head of a red-haired man, rising from the barrel like an apparition.

The stowaway rose to full height and stretched, easing the muscles so long cramped. His coat of mail was tarnished. A sword hung at his side.

As Señor Enciso choked, unable to find words to express his

shock and anger, the uninvited passenger pulled after him a large bloodhound of vicious aspect. Enciso drew back involuntarily.

Almost immediately the tall stowaway was encircled by an astonished group of soldiers and cavaliers, staring in silence.

Then Enciso found his voice, but it cracked with rage in the middle of his question.

"What are you doing here?"

Flushing slightly, the young man stepped forward and bowed low.

"I desire to ask the great commander's indulgence for this intrusion. The manner of my appearance, informal as it was, was not the result of desire, I assure you, but of dire necessity."

"I understand that." Enciso panted furiously. "You are a debtor."

"I am a debtor." He bowed again, with exaggerated courtesy. "I owe the shrewdest merchants in Santo Domingo. Ask anyone. Ask them if they know Vasco Núñez de Balboa. Ask them how much —"

"I do not need to ask them. I know the sort you are!" Enciso's eyes flashed scorn. What ill fortune! Despite every precaution, this rash fellow, this highhanded debtor had smuggled himself into the ship of the future Chief Judge Enciso.

"I have a strong hand and willing muscles, Señor Enciso. If you will accept me as one of your company, you will see for yourself. You will see —"

"I will see you in chains!" roared the irritated commander. "I will see you cast ashore on the first island we pass!"

There was a low murmuring around the group. All knew that the islands in this part of the Caribbean were uninhabited and without fresh water. It was, virtually, a death sentence for Balboa.

On the fringe of the group, Bartolomé Hurtado heard the sentence with even more alarm than the others. Having been instrumental in getting him aboard, he felt that he would be partly to blame if Balboa were cast upon a desert island.

Only Balboa remained calm and spoke again to Enciso, begging him to reconsider and requesting to enlist as a soldier.

Enciso pressed his lips tightly together. "What! You have the amazing hardihood to believe that I would countenance the escape of a debtor by taking him into my company! I tell you, Vasco Núñez de Balboa, you are both impudent and insane."

"But I have often fought against the Indians —"

"It is true." Bartolomé Hurtado stepped forward. "He is renowned for his valorous encounters with the natives. I have heard of his prowess."

"And I," said another.

"I, too," said a third.

It was apparent that the sympathies of his men were with the despicable debtor. Many of them, Enciso guessed, were probably acquainted with Vasco Núñez de Balboa, for he was a familiar if unimportant figure in Santo Domingo. Possibly, thought Enciso disdainfully, because that blazing mop of hair drew attention, or possibly because of the man's great stature, noticeable in any gathering.

Now was the time to assert his authority as commander of these men and as future alcalde mayor.

"No." He shook his head. "I cannot overlook this irregularity. Put him in chains!"

No one moved. Protestations increased in volume and sincerity. Enciso himself moved forward threateningly, but the vicious hound at Balboa's side bared his teeth fiercely.

Bartolomé Hurtado took advantage of the moment to mention that the dog was none other than the famous and ferocious Leonçico.

"He is as good as a man in an Indian campaign," said another soldier.

"It is true," said a cavalier, "that this man is a bankrupt farmer, but his good qualities outweigh that fact in my opinion."

"He is brave," continued Hurtado. "He is a good soldier. He is a master swordsman. He has with him the best-trained hound on the ship."

"Enlist them both!" came the cry.

Martin Fernández de Enciso, looking about at his sturdy cavaliers, saw that they were not only earnest in championing this debtor, but even enthusiastic. The bold manner of his appearance on shipboard had apparently enchanted them. They obviously admired his great build, his reputation as a fighter, and his surprisingly assured bearing. Grudgingly Enciso admitted to himself that he had never seen a more vigorous specimen of manhood. Outdoor life had made him muscular and lithe, and his face was tanned to a smooth gold. The commander, pale and soft from sedentary work, was indeed looking at his exact opposite. The sight did not please him in the least.

Nevertheless, the clamor favoring this absconding debtor was too great now to override. Enciso, never at best a decisive character, weakened. Very well, let the fellow remain. No doubt he could be employed to advantage in the new colony. No doubt his restless vitality indicated a mind much less developed. Enciso was a firm believer that all conceivable knowledge came from books and he was smugly certain that Vasco Núñez was not of a studious nature. When he was fully installed in his exalted office of alcalde mayor, he could soon put down this man by one means or another.

"Very well." Enciso's voice purred condescendingly. "I will accept you as one of my colonists, Vasco Núñez de Balboa. For this leniency I trust you will serve me well, you and your celebrated hound."

Vasco Núñez bowed low. His face showed none of the instinctive dislike he felt for this pompous scholar, but far back in his blue eyes humor glinted.

"Be assured of that. Leonçico and I will not forget this day."

Only Bartolomé Hurtado noted the roguish glint in his friend's eyes, and he felt uneasy. That certain look of Balboa's portended a clash of wills some time in the future.

CHAPTER IX

THE STRANGE BRIGANTINE

ENCISO'S TWO CARAVELS ARRIVED AT THE COAST OF TERRA FIRMA without mishap and sailed into the harbor of Cartagena. His vessels needed some small repairs and he hoped to procure fresh water. A number of men, including Balboa, were landed to work on the boat.

Scarcely had they begun, however, when they became aware that great numbers of natives were gathering at some distance, well-armed and apparently menacing.

"Our presence here, I perceive, is viewed with suspicion," commented Vasco Núñez wryly.

They continued their work unmolested for three days, however, for the Indians were apparently wary of attacking. No doubt, decided Balboa, they had had experience with Spaniards before.

"If we do not attack, they will not," he told Bartolomé Hurtado. "We must not show alarm."

He persuaded Hurtado to accompany him to a nearby river to fill a water cask.

"'Tis folly!" protested the soldier reluctantly. "If we go, we should go in an armed company."

"Indeed not," replied Balboa calmly. "The fact that we two go fearlessly should convince these restless natives of our peaceable intentions. Believe me, I know well the Indian mind."

"Near Santo Domingo, yes, where they have been well tamed!"

"Do you come?" demanded Balboa. "If not, I venture forth alone." His chin set stubbornly in a way Hurtado knew well, and his blue eyes flashed determination.

"I come — but I come with prayers."

On the river's margin they bent to fill the cask. Hurtado's eyes darted to the thickets near by and, as if his fearful expectation had drawn them, eleven savages bounded forth. Bending their bows and pointing arrows at the two Spaniards' breasts, they soon surrounded them.

"We are lost!" exclaimed Hurtado despairingly.

"Not yet," said Balboa, his eyes steady. "The arrows have not yet been discharged."

"Then before they are," begged Hurtado, "let us depart hence!" He made an attempt to break through the circle of Indians and run to the others who were mending the boat. Threateningly, the Indians pointed their arrows at his back.

"Return, Hurtado!" Balboa's voice rang out in such sharp, sure command that the other turned and hastily retraced his steps to his friend's side.

Vasco Núñez then spoke in a friendly tone to the savages in their own tongue. The fierceness on the dark faces gave way somewhat to astonishment that this stranger was acquainted with their language.

One of them spoke in reply. "Who are you and what seek you upon our shores?"

Balboa answered soothingly: "We are harmless people from far lands. We touch your shores of necessity to repair our vessels and to procure water for our people. Why are we thus accosted with warlike weapons? Conquest is not our goal. Nevertheless, be warned that any hostility will bring a host of our countrymen to wreak terrible vengeance. Therefore, let us meet in peace, I pray."

He continued to speak to them in like manner, alternating reassurance with threats should any mischief be done by the savages.

"Others of your people," the natives stated, "have invaded our lands and laid waste our homes. Our villages have been ravaged and our friends and relatives slain."

"We are not the same. We come in peace," reiterated Balboa.

He had almost convinced them when the success of the parley was jeopardized by the well-meant but ill-timed appearance of Enciso, who came with an armed force from his ship to rescue the two.

As he drew near, however, Balboa signaled him that all was well and he held his fire.

The Indians threw down their weapons then, and approached without hostility. During the days that the Spaniards remained on those shores, the natives generously supplied them with maize bread, salted fish and native drinks.

Enciso, however, gave little credit to Balboa for having won the friendship of the Indians, but preferred to think that his own arrival had so intimidated them that they were frightened into submission. The brave conduct of the stowaway debtor, however, did not escape the silent approval of the rest of the company.

One day, as Enciso was preparing to sail on in search of Ojeda's settlement, another European ship entered the harbor and anchored. Enciso's two caravels were filled with excitement. Whose ship was it?

The commander immediately boarded the vessel, taking with him an armed escort of his best warriors for protection. Balboa and Hurtado were among them.

To his amazement and alarm, Enciso discovered that the men aboard the brigantine were the same who had embarked months before with Ojeda for the new settlement. His suspicions were aroused. He accused the men, who were in a wretched, half-starved condition, of having mutinied against Ojeda and seized the vessel to desert in.

Francisco Pizarro, commander of the thirty-five men on the ship, denied this vehemently.

"We are the unfortunate survivors of the colony at San Sebastian, but we are not deserters. We have experienced great sufferings and misery, as you well can see, Señor Enciso."

Pizarro's gaunt face with shadowed weary eyes and hollow cheeks was sufficient proof, but Enciso needed further convincing. Pizarro then produced his letter patent, signed by Alonso de Ojeda. This made him governor of the colony in Ojeda's absence.

"But where is Ojeda?" demanded Enciso impatiently. "Why did he turn over the command of the colony to you?"

"Ojeda," said Pizarro, "is on his way to Santo Domingo. As a matter of fact, he should have arrived there long ere now."

"But why? For what cause? It was understood between us that he was to remain in the settlement until I arrived."

"I will tell you," replied Pizarro wearily. "It is a long story and a dreadful one, but lest I tire you, I will shorten it."

Indeed, the tale told by Ojeda's lieutenant was a bitter one. Landing at Terra Firma, the company of colonists had been successfully resisted by the Carib Indians.

"Their arrows," said Francisco Pizarro, "are steeped in deadly poison. If a man should receive nothing more than a scratch, he would die in fearful agony. We lost seventy soldiers. Among them the gallant navigator, Juan de la Cosa, who displayed a wondrous courage in his last moments."

Juan de la Cosa! Balboa was saddened as he heard this. He remembered the veteran pilot with rare affection. What unhappy news for his nephew, Sebastian Bernalo, back in Spain! No more would he receive letters and souvenirs from his adored uncle in Terra Firma. No longer would Juan de la Cosa's sister and nieces deck themselves in the pearls he had sent them. Balboa experienced a genuine sorrow. But Juan de la Cosa had died courageously. That was important — to die valiantly, so that men might wreathe the fact of one's death with admiration. Vasco Núñez de Balboa swore to himself that when his own time came, he, too, would meet the dark adventure gloriously.

But Francisco Pizarro was still unfolding his sorry tale, and Balboa thrust aside his emotions to listen.

The loss of Juan de la Cosa had left Ojeda in unknown waters without a dependable guide. Therefore he was not able to reach his destination, the Gulf of Urabá, but finally landed just east of it.

"There we erected a stockade and a number of palm-thatched dwellings. Ojeda named the settlement San Sebastian."

Enciso nodded. "After the saint martyred by arrows."

"Aye. He aspired to invoke divine aid against the venomous missiles of the savages." Pizarro shrugged. "His hope was vain. The death toll from the native arrows mounted daily. There was a food shortage and we could not go into the interior in the hope of replenishing our supplies, because of the terrible vigilance of the infidels."

"But surely — " began Enciso.

The skin tightened on Pizarro's lean face and his eyes seemed to be staring at the beach scenes he described.

"We were menaced as well by sickness. It was not long before starvation, disease and fevers, as well as the hostile arrows, had reduced our number to less than sixty men, most of them weak and impotent as soldiers."

Enciso's countenance grew longer and longer as the story of the fate of his precious colony unfolded. His plump face settled in folds of despair and his beringed fingers fumbled nervously with the elegant brooch at his throat.

"And then?" he croaked. "What did Ojeda do then?"

"He was dangerously wounded. The men were threatening to seize one of the three remaining ships and return to Española. To forestall such revolt, Ojeda decided to take a few men and go himself. He hoped to hasten your coming, Señor Enciso, and to secure more reinforcements. He left me in charge, as this letter patent shows."

"But you did not stay," protested Enciso angrily. "You should have remained."

"It was understood," replied Pizarro, "that if our commander failed to return in fifty days, we were free to return to Española or to settle elsewhere." His lips twisted. "He did not return, though we waited even longer than that."

"Mercy of heaven! He had ample time to reach Santo Domingo. That means —" Beads of perspiration gathered on Enciso's brow. "He has been shipwrecked."

"Aye," Pizarro nodded, "so it would appear."

"And you set sail in the remaining two caravels. Where — where is the second?"

Pizarro's voice was listless. "There was a great storm and it sank with all hands. We saw our comrades perish."

Balboa was filled with pity for the unfortunate starving men. It was apparent that they needed food badly. Why did not Señor Enciso attend to these pressing physical needs, instead of insisting on an immediate accounting from Ojeda's brave lieutenant? He studied Pizarro's narrow face. A few years older than Balboa, he was in the prime of manhood. There was a look of ruthlessness about him, honed by the recent hardships.

There was in his black eyes a stubborn determination to endure and put the print of his name on history's page. Courage he had, and cruelty. Balboa passed over the cruelty and approved the courage.

Enciso, pacing the deck, returned frowning.

"Your story may be true. Nevertheless, I shall see for myself. You and your men shall return with us to San Sebastian."

Pizarro's men protested in horror. They begged to be permitted to proceed to Santo Domingo. They repeated the list of perils, recounted again their dreadful sufferings. But to no avail. Señor Enciso had no desire to return ignominiously to Santo Domingo whence he had started so brilliantly. He had arranged with Ojeda to go to the settlement and he meant to do so.

Annoyed by the vociferous objections of Pizarro and his followers, he took the command away from Ojeda's lieutenant, using his authority as chief judge.

The ships made sail for San Sebastian.

But scarcely had the fleet rounded the Punta de Caribana, which led into the Gulf of Urabá, when the caravel of Enciso struck a submerged rock and sank.

CHAPTER X

FURTHER MISFORTUNES

WHILE THE SWIFT CURRENTS AND TURBULENT WAVES BATTERED the sinking ship, the men flung themselves overboard into the sea, where they either swam about as best they could or clung to stray pieces of wreckage.

Fortunately, no lives were lost in the disaster. All managed to reach the brigantine of Pizarro safely. Enciso was in great despair, however, for the horses, swine and great stores of colonial supplies were swept away. Truly it was a calamity, for the only provisions saved were twelve barrels of meal, a few cheeses and a little biscuit bread. Indeed, the men themselves escaped half-clothed and poorly armed.

Some of Pizarro's men shook their heads morbidly. "These shores are cursed. Even nature fights with the infidels to keep us from them."

One of them, Fernando Múñoz, spoke his opinion aloud for the depressed Enciso to hear.

"It is an ill omen. Truly, it is a warning to turn back to Santo Domingo."

Enciso seized this as an excuse to spill forth his furious frustration. His whole frame quivered with his tumultuous emotions. He glowered at the poor soldier as if he held him responsible for the shipwreck.

"Another word of turning back — and it is chains for you! Chains and starvation in the foulest part of the hold. Think you I will return to Santo Domingo in this sorry state? No, come what may, here we stay until fortune smiles again."

Out of range of Enciso's sensitive ears, Vasco Núñez murmured to Bartolomé: "Should Lady Fortune smile on that face, I should have little respect for her judgment."

Bartolomé Hurtado doubled in laughter at the quip. Enciso's sharp eyes fell upon him, and he roared the length of the deck.

"Bartolomé Hurtado, why are you merry at such a time?"

The soldier's laughter gurgled to nought in his throat. His face went crimson.

"I — I —"

"What's that?" bellowed the commander. "I cannot hear you at that distance. Come forward!"

Uncertainly, Hurtado stepped forward. Balboa, ever a loyal comrade, came with him.

"If it please you, 'twas I who made him merry."

Enciso glared. "You? How?"

"He was saying," interrupted Hurtado, fearing that Balboa's frank tongue might send them both to the hold dungeon, "that anyone who thought we would turn back now to Santo Domingo was lacking in intelligence and valor. The notion, he said, was amusing. I, too, thought as much."

The commander's anger subsided, but he still glared at the two.

"Well, at least, I am glad to find you do not favor a fainthearted course, even though your laughter was badly timed."

Several years' prosperous practice of the law in Santo Domingo had come to nothing as a result of the sinking of his largest caravel, but there was more misfortune to come.

Upon landing at the site of San Sebastian, the colonists of Martin Fernández de Enciso were confronted by a discouraging scene. The fort and the adjacent dwellings had been leveled by fire. Only a few charred ruins remained.

"Indians," said Francisco Pizarro. "They are unrelenting in their revenge, the blasted infidels!"

Conflicting emotions played over Enciso's full face, but he said with a show of firmness: "We will rebuild the settlement."

So, unsheltered from the fierce heat of the tropical sun and unprotected from the raw nights and frequent chilling cloudbursts, the work of thrusting back the wilderness began. Labor as they did, however, they accomplished little. In a short time they found themselves struggling for a bare existence, not too successfully. Their depleted provisions gave out entirely.

Occasionally they were able to capture a peccary, a kind of wild swine which roamed the land, but the hostile Indians soon made hunting expeditions impossible.

Pizarro's followers told awful tales of the agony caused by the poisoned arrows of the savages. The unpleasant realism of these recitals induced extreme caution in everyone. No one desired to be a target for a venomous dart, even though starvation was imminent.

At last, when they were forced to subsist on nothing more than palm nuts, Enciso called for a company of a hundred men.

"We will penetrate into the interior to forage for supplies," he told them, but his voice had lost its former assurance and bluster. He himself had lost much of his excess weight and, along with it, his self-confidence. The skin of his face and neck was wrinkled and baggy where the flesh had gone from beneath. The rings hung loose on his fingers. All the rest were thinner, too, but the near-starvation showed most on the formerly rotund Enciso.

Balboa appeared longer and more rangy, but aside from the sharpness of his cheekbones seemed little the worse for his sufferings and deprivations.

Listening to the commander's plan, Balboa's eyes went with

approval to the eaglelike profile of Pizarro. The man was even thinner than when first they had met, but with something of the enduring sharpness of a well-tempered sword. The perils and hardships of their position had only succeeded in making him more alert.

Balboa volunteered as one of the hundred, along with Fernando Múñoz, with whom he had become better acquainted since coming ashore. Múñoz was rather a rough character, not a nobleman, with a hardiness about him that Balboa liked. Bartolomé Hurtado elected to remain at the settlement with Pizarro, who reluctantly agreed to take charge while Enciso was away. It was clear, however, that he chafed at his waiting role and would far rather have joined the foraging party.

Scarcely was Enciso's company out of sight of the harbor than three Indians leapt brazenly upon them from the woods and discharged all the arrows in their quivers with a swiftness that paralyzed the Spaniards. Several of the men were wounded before the savages fled into the woods as quickly as they had come.

Stunned by the attack the company hastened back to San Sebastian, carrying their wounded with them. Several expired on the way, suffering great agony.

Vasco Núñez tried to train his ears not to hear their pitiful shrieks, and for the first time began to share the anger of his countrymen against the natives of Terra Firma. Surely the poisoning of arrows was a cruel and inhuman thing. In the heat of his compassion for his suffering comrades, he refused to think what would have befallen the three Indians had they fallen unarmed into the hands of the Spaniards.

Completely disheartened now, Enciso did not know what to do. He still did not wish to return in defeat to Santo Domingo, ruined financially and the probable object of ridicule. But it was clear that to remain longer in San Sebastian would mean the complete annihilation of his colony. But where to go? Might not the same disasters attend him anywhere else?

With one exception, his men were clamoring to return to the comparatively civilized Isla Española. The only man who seemed to be as reluctant as Enciso to return was Vasco Núñez de Balboa. The reason for his reluctance was obvious. Should he return to Santo Domingo, his creditors would be after him in full cry and prison would doubtless be his lot. He cast about in his mind for a way out.

His countrymen, made desperate by hardships, were growing more and more unruly in their conduct toward Enciso, whom they found a weak and indecisive leader. They showed him only a bare civility, and Balboa feared mutiny. Although he had no more respect nor admiration for Enciso than many of the others, Balboa was forced by circumstances to side with the leader for the present.

Where could they go — if not back to Santo Domingo?

An inspiration struck him. He stepped forward, separating himself from the grumbling, dissatisfied men, and bowed low before Señor Enciso.

"I know a place on this coast where we might settle." His full vibrant voice drew the attention of the Spaniards and the muttering died away. "Many years ago when I sailed with Rodrigo de Bastidas, we explored the entire Gulf of Urabá. A river flows into it on the western side, which the natives call Darien. The land is fertile and I have heard that gold is abundant."

Much as Enciso disliked the impudent debtor, who had forced a place for himself among his colonists, at this moment he beamed upon him. If what Balboa said were true, it would certainly be a wonderful place to settle. Moreover, the rest of the men, he saw with satisfaction, were full of interest, although not fully relinquishing the determination to return to Santo Domingo.

"But what of the savages?" inquired Fernando Múñoz. "Are they warlike?"

Vasco Núñez nodded. "Aye, they are warlike." Seeing the discouragement in every face, he added: "But they do not use poisoned arrows."

After their recent experiences, this was good news indeed. All in all, the country of Darien sounded like an earthly paradise. The prospect of ample provisions was indeed pleasant. The promise of gold was a shining lure to every Spaniard. After all, perhaps the high hopes with which they had begun this colonizing expedition might yet be fulfilled. And to hear that the natives on the Darien shores did not employ venomous darts — that settled the matter!

The words of Balboa transformed the grumbling dejected company into a highhearted band of adventurers once more. They cheered him enthusiastically and Enciso, since he himself was profiting, did not resent the ovation.

He questioned Balboa further and, having learned there was an Indian village already established on the river bank, he gave orders to set sail, without delay, for Darien.

CHAPTER XI

ON THE SHORES OF DARIEN

BALBOA STOOD A LITTLE APART FROM THE OTHERS AS THE SHIP approached the shores of Darien. His eyes caressed the green banks of the narrow river bed, lingered on the rolling fertile country beyond, then lifted in greeting to the lofty mountains pushing toward the blue sky.

It was like coming home again to reach these banks once more. It was like seeing an old and treasured friend. Vasco Núñez wiped the moisture from his forehead, but even as he did so he was not aware of the day's heat. All the hurried sounds of preparing to anchor, the excited shouts of his companions, his ears heard but his mind did not absorb.

Ten years ago he had stood, not upon the deck of Enciso's caravel but upon that of Rodrigo de Bastidas. Sebastian Bernalo had been with him, and Andrés Garavito. Now Sebastian was back in Spain and Andrés — where was Andrés now? He had remained in Santo Domingo when Bartolomé Hurtado and Vasco Núñez had turned to farming, scorning to join them at such an occupation. He was a soldier, he had said. He would dig gold and not beets. He was a fighter of men, not of weeds. The last Vasco Núñez had heard, he had joined the expedition of Diego de Nicuesa, rival of Ojeda, who also was founding a colony in Terra Firma. Well, Balboa shrugged, Andrés Garavito had been right about farming. There had been no future in it — that is, no prosperous future.

Bartolomé Hurtado came to stand beside him. "Ten years

71

ago when we approached these shores, I knew you only by sight, Vasco Núñez."

"That is true." Balboa nodded, smiling.

"That was before the shipwreck when you saved my life."

"You are still exaggerating, I see, about that. You were not in any danger of drowning, my friend."

"But I was," insisted Bartolomé.

"Well, if so, any debt you may have owed to me has been fully repaid. If it were not for your aid and that of Juan de Valdivia I should not be here now." He turned his shining eyes toward the land. "And to be here now, at Darien, that is all I ask."

"I could ask for more," said Bartolomé. "I could ask for fewer natives in that village, for one thing." He gestured toward the Indian huts on the bank. The inhabitants were running to and fro in great consternation, gesticulating in both fear and anger as the caravel came nearer. Indian women, clad in bright cotton skirts and carrying babies, ran toward the woods beyond the settlement. Children scurried after, their naked brown bodies glistening in the bright sun.

"And I," said Fernando Múñoz, coming up, "could ask that these infidel warriors, marshaling their forces yonder, do not use poisoned arrows."

A friend of his, Martín Zamudio, a soldier from Biscay, crossed himself fervently. "You say that ten years ago when you touched these shores they did not, Vasco Núñez de Balboa. Let us pray that they are a backward tribe and have not learned new ways from fiercer nations."

Indeed, the prospects were none too bright. Even if the Indians did not make use of poisoned arrows, as Balboa had said, they were more than five hundred strong and greatly outnumbered the Spaniards. Nevertheless, no one suggested turning back, for where would they go? What else was there to do, except remain and fight as best they could?

Enciso, looking slightly pale and none too confident, gave orders for every able-bodied warrior to go ashore in the boats.

"We will draw up our forces on yonder summit," he said, indicating a hill to the left.

Able-bodied or not, weak or comparatively strong, all volunteered to go ashore. And not only the soldiers went, but also the gaunt hounds, made even more ferocious by near-starvation. Among them, of course, was the most formidable of them all, Leonçico, Balboa's dog.

"This is an important moment, Leonçico," whispered Balboa into the animal's scarred alert ear. "You must live up to your reputation. Remember the proud family you come from. Remember your father, the great Beçerrico. You must prove yourself even more valorous than he."

Martín Zamudio grinned wryly. "And do you think for one moment, Vasco Núñez, that he understands you?"

Balboa set his shoulders with dignity, as much as he could muster in the rocking boat. "Assuredly yes, my friend. Other dogs might not, but Leonçico is not an ordinary beast."

Drawing the boats up on the sand, they arrayed themselves on the hillock as Enciso had instructed. But before launching into battle, they yielded to his request that they kneel and pray. Enciso begged the aid of the Blessed Virgin, promising in return to name the settlement that they would establish after her and also that each man would send an offering of gold to her shrine in Seville known by the name of Santa María della Antigua.

As they rose from their knees, supposing that now the hostilities might commence, Enciso halted them. They must take another vow, more practical at the moment.

"Each of you must swear by all that is holy," he intoned, in his most precise legal manner, "that you will not retreat, no matter what transpires."

Fernando Múñoz and the soldiers of Pizarro shifted uneasily.

"Not even," asked Fernando in a thin voice, "if the natives make use of venomous arrows and darts?"

"No retreat, though they employ thunderbolts and lightning," shrilled Enciso. He glared at Fernando Múñoz, who bowed his head.

One by one, they took the oath.

Shields on their left arms and halberds in readiness, the Spaniards waited for the signal to attack.

"Now!"

They charged, necessity having made them desperate. Shrieking, they plunged down the hill at the Indians who met them with all the fierceness of those who defend their homes against invasion. But the wooden arrows and clubs of the natives were no match for the steel of the Spaniards. Moreover, the sight of the snarling, rapacious hounds horrified them even more. Their lines broke. The native warriors scattered. They fled toward the woods into which, not long before, their women and children had disappeared. In an incredibly short space of time, the Indian village was deserted.

Triumphantly Enciso, who had not been foremost in battle, marched forward and took possession of the native huts.

How overjoyed the Spaniards were to discover that Balboa's words concerning the fertility of this land were indeed true. For here was the evidence in the blessed form of food, ready for eating. Yucca and casaba bread, native melons, fruits, fowls and fermented beverages made of native fruits and grains.

Immediately a feast was ordered and, although still fearing

possible attack by the Indians, they gratefully appeased their hunger.

"Never has food tasted so good!" declared Balboa. Even as he said it he remembered the heaped table of Don Gaspard de Vorales, back in Spain, and how the same thought had come to him then, when the delicious odors had been those of familiar foods. Hunger, he thought, can make even the most unfamiliar foods gratifying to the stomach.

"What fruits these be, I know not," sighed Bartolomé Hurtado. "But whatever they are, they are wonderful."

"Aye, wonderful!" agreed Juan de Valdivia. Ordinarily fastidious in his habits, he was now stuffing his mouth, forgetting all propriety of table manners.

Vasco Núñez looked up from the loaf of bread he was tearing apart, his eyes twinkling as he watched Valdivia's unaccustomed greed.

"What is that earthy-skinned thing you are eating?" he asked curiously. "Is it good?"

"Heaven itself could afford nothing better!" He held up the potato, showing the white inside. "I found these among some dying coals of fire. Half are uncooked and taste something like green chestnuts. Only sweeter, I think. But those that are cooked — ah!" He rolled his eyes, smacking his lips ecstatically.

"Give me one," said Balboa. "I must taste this ambrosia."

Reluctantly, Juan de Valdivia parted with it. "Oh, very well, Vasco Núñez. I can see I was too enthusiastic in my praise. You will have me starving again, with your demands."

"Not likely." Balboa laughed and bit into the vegetable. His eyes widened appreciatively. "Ah, you underestimated. These are even better than you said." He took another bite.

"I wonder how they are grown. On trees, do you think? No, they are more like a turnip. No doubt they grow in the ground — a root plant. We must investigate the fields and see if we can find out about them."

"How quickly the soldier gives way to the farmer!" Juan de Valdivia smiled, his words coming thickly from his stuffed mouth.

Bartolomé Hurtado lifted an earthen jar of native brew. He put it to his lips appreciatively.

"This also — this is good for the dry and thirsty throat."

But Enciso, taking counsel with Diego del Corral, a fellow lawyer, put the feasting to an end as soon as his own hunger was fully assuaged. Night had fallen and he feared the men might grow lazy and sluggish from overeating, especially since they had had so little previously.

"The natives may yet be lying in wait for us," he said, looking over his shoulder apprehensively at the dark shadows sprawling from the strange tropical vegetation. "Perhaps, under cover of darkness, they will attack. Half of our number must lie awake throughout the night."

Despite Enciso's reasonable fears, however, the night passed peacefully. Those on watch reported neither sight nor sound of any Indian.

In the early morning, while the mists still rose wraithlike from the valley, a party of the Spaniards set out along the river to the woods a mile inland. They suspected that the savages might still be hiding among the dense foliage of the forest.

Moving cautiously under the protection of their shields, they searched every thicket. No Indians. Only birds of many colors, large and small, fluttered chattering among the leaves.

As they were about to return to the village, a shout went up from Fernando Múñoz and Francisco Pizarro. The former had stumbled over a log, falling headlong into a pile of branches and heaped leaves. Underneath, a wide deep hole had been dug out and there, cleverly hidden by the retreating natives, were gold and copper ornaments, necklaces, anklets, breast plates and beautifully wrought bracelets. There were also bright woven coverlets and utensils of polished wood and pottery.

Excitedly, the Spaniards fell upon this loot. It was encouraging evidence of the richness of the country to which they had come.

Back in the village Enciso took charge, estimating the worth of the findings at ten thousand castellanos. It was five times the amount he had put into this colonization project and it seemed that fortune was indeed smiling on him. His fingers caressed the precious metal, smoothed the lengths of native cloth, fondled the artfully wrought bowls.

"Doubtless the gold comes from tribes further inland," said Balboa to Juan de Valdivia. "The natives here in this fertile valley exchange food products raised in their fields for these precious ornaments. Back in the mountains there must be great treasure." His eyes glowed. "I mean to make a journey into the unexplored interior as soon as possible."

"Aye, and I shall go with you!" Valdivia responded. Then he looked around him. "But in the meantime, the practical Enciso will want to build a town. His prestige suffers from being housed in an ordinary native hut like the rest of us poor mortals."

Juan de Valdivia had spoken truly. The work of building the town was begun immediately. They left most of the Indian dwellings intact, but cleared a place in the center of the settlement for the traditional plaza or public square. Surrounding it, they erected crude wooden cabins, palm thatched, a cabildo where official business was to be transacted, and a smelting house where the gold was to be melted down for division among them and the royal fifth taken out to be sent to His Majesty, King Ferdinand.

Finally, with a great show of authority, Enciso ordered another building to be put up in the plaza. It was small, gloomy, and strongly built.

Balboa and Hurtado, who had been assigned to work the fields while the building was going on, rode in one twilight just as the crude door was being fastened in place.

"And what," asked Balboa of the workmen, "is that stuffy looking structure?"

Enciso came forward pompously. "That, Vasco Núñez de Balboa, is the prison. And why shouldn't it be stuffy? Should prisons be palaces? Jails are for the criminal and indigent — as debtors, for instance."

Vasco Núñez bowed. "I understand. Nevertheless, the sight is discouraging. I had not thought such a thing necessary among us. For when one prepares for the worst — behold, the worst occurs. One buys a sword and soon there is blood upon it. One builds a prison and soon there are victims to fill it. I fear, good señor, that you are of a pessimistic turn of mind."

"And with reason. I know the foul passions that lurk in men. I know their greed, their impudence, their blood lust."

"But do you not know their kindness, too?" asked Vasco Núñez mildly. "Their comradeship, their endurance and their valor?"

The commander's face worked angrily. "Do you preach to me, you stowaway in a cask? Do you question my authority as alcalde?" He steadied his voice with difficulty. "Let it suffice you that every civilized community must have a place of detention for those who menace the rights of others."

That evening when all were gathered together in the plaza the new settlement was named — with much lengthy legal intonation by Señor Enciso — Santa María la Antigua del Darien.

Vasco Núñez and Martín Zamudio walked back to their huts together, yawning wearily.

"I hope these meetings of Enciso aren't going to be a regular thing," said Martín, stretching his great frame.

"I hope not. If so, we'll all be too worn out to do a decent day's work either in cultivating or in hunting Indians and gold."

Martín Zamudio shook his head gloomily. "Enciso has stuffed his mind with so many long words and phrases they're bound to overflow."

CHAPTER XII

UNTIL THE KING'S PLEASURE BE KNOWN

ENCISO'S FIGURE BECAME PUDGY AGAIN AS THE DAYS PASSED, AND his manner became more overbearing. For long hours at a time he would shut himself up in his house, the most pretentious dwelling in the settlement, and pore over his law books and ledgers. To him these books were in many ways as precious as the gold he sought. For he loved power and authority. His life, except for the past few months, had been spent among litigants in Santo Domingo, among other lawyers, notaries and judges who flourished everywhere at this period. These men collected fees, juggled accounts and so overburdened the country with laws that the colonists were confused and baffled. Try as they might, they could not help breaking many of them.

The result was litigation, fines and imprisonment. No person in Isla Española could hope to follow the ordinary pursuits of business or pleasure without becoming involved, some way or other, in a lawsuit.

Martin Fernández de Enciso had grown prosperous defending or prosecuting such persons in court. But although he had done very well for himself, he had not reached the position of affluence and power that he craved. That, he felt, could best be reached in Terra Firma where men like himself could set up a government as despotic as that of any reigning prince in Europe. In fact, it was with this idea in mind that he had invested his savings in the undertaking of Ojeda who had received a royal grant to colonize and conquer a territory nearly as large as the whole of Spain.

So Enciso was busy now making laws. Often, when passing by his cabin, Balboa would see him sitting in the cool of a verandah or hunched up in a seat by the window, surrounded by rolls of parchment and barricaded by his books. In the heat of the day, while others might be taking their siesta, Enciso wrote continuously, his little eyes gleaming with a terrible satisfaction. Often, too, long after the tropic night had dropped its black mantle and the colonists were snoring in their huts, Balboa would be aware of a shaft of light fluttering toward the jungle from Enciso's house.

Balboa would smile to himself half in exasperation, half in wry amusement. So the good Enciso was still awake, was he, and still writing? He could picture the lawyer, pausing now and again to resharpen his quill pen or replenish his ink.

In less than a week Enciso had made more laws for his handful of followers than King Ferdinand and his court had made for the entire Spanish Empire.

Balboa returned from hunting wild boar one afternoon, tired from his long tramp through the jungle, when he perceived a crowd gathered in the plaza. Every man in the expedition was there, and all faces were turned toward the house of Enciso.

As he drew nearer he could hear the lawyer's voice resounding above the uneasy shuffling of feet. Across the still air came the first distinguishable words of a speech that was being delivered with all the impressive skill of a trained orator. Although a small man, Enciso had a persuasive, resonant voice, and he loved to use it.

He stood now upon a little balcony flush with the street. He was pouring a drink of water which he gulped down hurriedly, then cried:

"Men of Darien, the time has come when we can no longer govern ourselves loosely, or regulate our conduct by chance. We must have laws and abide by them. We must have authority vested in a practical man of affairs."

"Aye," agreed Diego del Corral, elbowing to the front of the crowd, "you speak truly, master."

Enciso paused to smile broadly. "Are you all of the same opinion?" Before anyone could reply, he went on hastily, "I trust that you are. But whether or not, beginning this day, laws which I have very carefully drawn up shall be put into effect. I say this because I have been duly authorized by the crown, not only to make the laws but to enforce them. I am your alcalde, your judge and arbitrator. I shall rule firmly, but justly." He cleared his throat and took up one of several parchment rolls. "Now hear ye what I have written."

Impressively unrolling it, Enciso read in sonorous tones his new law respecting all gold or treasure, acquired in whatsoever manner by any member or members of the expedition. Such gold or treasure, the law decreed, must be brought to Enciso himself at all times, under any and all circumstances, and by him weighed, appraised, evaluated and divided.

One fifth, the royal fifth, should be set aside for the crown. Of the four-fifths remaining, each man should have his just share after there had been taken from it an amount, not clearly stipulated, to defray the administrative costs of the government. Failure to obey this law, said Enciso warningly, would be punished by imprisonment and death.

As Balboa listened incredulously, he watched the faces of the men around him. The first shock of understanding having subsided, the expressions of bewilderment and dismay having gone, anger was dark on nearly every countenance. Here and there were exceptions — Enciso's confidants in this matter, no doubt. One of these was Diego del Corral, whose face clearly showed his approval.

For his own part, Balboa experienced merely a feeling of extreme contempt, mingled with a certain pity, for the officious lawyer. He had had dealings before in Santo Domingo with such gentlemen as Enciso. The lawyers and notaries and process servers had made his life unbearable toward the end of his experiment with farming. He had become too intimately acquainted with their pettifogging methods, their unfair practices, their unscrupulous and underhanded tricks to have any pleasant illusions regarding them. For that reason he had never, from their first moment of meeting, either liked or trusted Enciso. He could not forget how the lawyer had threatened to cast him ashore upon an uninhabited isle in the Caribbean without water or food.

Yes, he thoroughly despised all lawyers and notaries as a class — except the admirable and lovable Don Rodrigo de Bastidas, his former commander. Bastidas had dealt fairly with his men. Had he not given each one a bonus in addition to the liberal percentage of the treasure taken? Had there been a single complaint among his followers? No. How different it would be in Darien! When administrative costs of governing the colony had been deducted, when fines had been paid, when everything that the shrewd Enciso could think of had been taken out, the colonists would receive a share so small that it would scarcely be worth considering.

Disgusted at the turn of events, although he had been somewhat prepared, Balboa drew apart from the crowd and went thoughtfully on his way. He was too tired to listen any longer to the laws that Enciso had made for his own personal aggrandizement. He had hoped, above all things, to find enough gold in this new land to pay his debts. As a debtor, he dared return neither to Isla Española nor to Spain. The future looked bleak indeed for him and for all common soldiers at Darien.

Balboa sat down in the shade at his hut to rest. Leonçico, who had followed him in his unsuccessful foray into the jungle for wild boar, sat down beside him and licked his hand. The dog was sensitive to any change in his master's mood. He shoved his cold muzzle against his owner's arm and growled.

Suddenly both dog and man stood up. Between the young palm trees shading the southern end of the plaza hurried the figures of the colonists. They were coming this way. The noise of their approach was a confusing sound of angry steps and high-pitched voices. At their head strode Zamudio, an axe over one shoulder, and his cheeks puffing with indignation.

He shouted to Balboa as soon as he came within earshot.

"Have you deserted us?"

His comrades pressing impatiently behind him, Zamudio hurried to where Balboa and Leonçico stood.

"Have you heard the laws?" he bellowed.

Balboa stooped over to pat Leonçico's bristling head.

"Down! Down, Leonçico!" Then to Zamudio: "I heard the first one. It was enough. I could bear no more."

"The lawyer is mad!" roared Zamudio. "Neither fit to lead us nor to rule us. We have no intention of submitting to these outrages. We will not be robbed. We have our rights. We have come to ask if you will be our alcalde mayor."

"Aye!" shouted the men eagerly. "Aye! Alcalde mayor!"

Such a possibility had not occurred to Balboa. For a moment he faced them, his eyes not seeing them, but opened very wide and his lips curiously puckered. All at once he was back on his farm at Salvatierre dreaming once more the dreams of a conquistador. Watching the unrolling drama of exploration and conquest.

At last he could do the things he had always wanted to do: know the unknown, explore the far horizons for the cities of golden splendor of which Marco Polo had written. He, also, would seek the fabulous beings, the strange animals, the exotic flowers and plants that were to be found in Cathay. He might even, good fortune attending him, discover again for Christianity and the world the Island of the Seven Cities.

So absorbed was Balboa with these glamorous pictures that he had not heard Zamudio speak again, nor was he aware of Hurtado affectionately gripping his arm. Leonçico was still growling his displeasure at all the hubbub, however, and was beginning to show his teeth.

Then Zamudio asked, annoyed: "What, do you fear Enciso? Is that why you will give no answer?"

"Not so." Balboa shook his head.

"Then what delays your answer? What troubles you?"

"Nothing."

"We will hold an election," proposed Juan de Valdivia. "That is the fair way in such things."

From the center of the crowd the deep voice of a Castilian soldier shouted: "Two alcaldes instead of one would be better. What do you say we elect both and a regidor besides?"

To this last proposal everyone agreed. Led by the Castilian soldier, the crowd proceeded immediately to the cabildo where, despite the horrified protests of Enciso and a few of his adherents, a vote was taken.

The two alcaldes elected were Vasco Núñez de Balboa and the fiery Biscayan, Martín Zamudio. Bartolomé Hurtado was chosen chief constable and Juan de Valdivia, regidor.

But no sooner were the results announced than a dispute arose concerning the various duties of the alcaldes. Also how long were they to serve? Who was to act as chief one, or mayor? In case of attack by natives, who was to be military leader?

More and more questions were asked, and more and more differences of opinion arose. At midnight, confused and weary at hearing so much bickering, Balboa called his dog to heel, linked his arm through Hurtado's and hurried off to bed.

The next day the disputes became even more violent. It was now proposed that only one alcalde be chosen. A new election should be held at once, many said. Some said that since this was rightfully Nicuesa's territory, he should be summoned to rule over them. A minority spoke for returning the outraged Enciso to power.

"The way to settle this," claimed Francisco Pizarro, "is to reinstate Enciso until the pleasure of the king be known."

But those who desired the return of Enciso were fewer than those who wished the present leaders to remain in office.

Another day wore on — and another. Weeks passed and still no decision could be reached. The controversy reached its height. Tempers flamed. Quarrels reached the point of open violence. It began to seem that despite all efforts on the part of Balboa and Zamudio to pacify them, the colonists would plunge into a civil strife, dueling and battling until neither rulers nor ruled would survive.

In the midst of this deepening conflict there suddenly fell across the air one morning the thundering rumble of cannon shots from the opposite side of the Gulf of Urabá. Black smoke from signal fires rose from distant hills.

That meant one thing. Another European ship was in the gulf. Excitedly firing their own cannon in reply, the colonists swarmed to the shore.

Breathlessly they waited until two ships, sails chalky white against the blue tropical sky, bore down upon them.

CHAPTER XIII

ENTER RODRIGO DE COLMENARES

THE TWO EUROPEAN SHIPS ANCHORED OFF THE DARIEN SHORE AND boats were put out from them. The colonists waited with mingled emotions to learn who the commander might be. Was it Nicuesa, perhaps, come to claim his rights to his land grant and assert his authority?

It was not Nicuesa, but Rodrigo de Colmenares, his officer, who had come from Santo Domingo with supplies and reinforcements for his superior.

"We have met many misfortunes," said Rodrigo de Colmenares. "Storms at sea have battered our ships. Natives on shore have taken horrible toll with poisoned arrows. We stopped at San Sebastian, only to find the settlement in ruins."

"Aye, we have lately come from thence," said Enciso and told Colmenares what he knew regarding Ojeda's fate. Francisco Pizarro stepped forward to corroborate his statements. "The land was barren and unfruitful," continued Enciso, "and the natives used poisonous darts. Therefore, we sought more fertile lands and less savage natives. Here we have subdued the Indians and are trading with them. We are carving a fine settlement out of this bitter wilderness."

Vasco Núñez de Balboa allowed him to talk as if he were still in command of the colony, but Enciso's followers were not long in informing Rodrigo de Colmenares of the real state of affairs.

Colmenares frowned and stroked his chin. "Neither one of

you is entitled to rule this settlement," he said finally. "As you know, these are Nicuesa's lands and so are subject to his authority as governor." He strode up and down the cabildo, eyes staring at the floor. "If only I could locate Nicuesa — then your problems and mine would be solved. Diego de Nicuesa is noted for his gracious manners and winning ways. You could not ask for a better governor."

"Aye." Many of the colonists nodded. "We have heard nothing but praise of Diego de Nicuesa. We would be well pleased if he should come and rule over us here in Darien."

But the adherents of both Enciso and Vasco Núñez de Balboa remained silent. Should Nicuesa be found, the lawyer was aware that he would have to give up his own claim to authority. Moreover, had he not been the friend and financial backer of Nicuesa's bitter rival, Ojeda? It was unlikely that Nicuesa would look upon him with favor.

Once again Balboa found himself sharing the opinion of Enciso. He had no wish to see Nicuesa brought back to the settlement as governor. But he remained silent, for if these were Nicuesa's lands, that cavalier surely had a right to them legally.

Balboa's friends, however, were loud in their protests. Bartolomé Hurtado, Fernando Múñoz, Martín Zamudio and Juan de Valdivia clamored that the colony of Darien was doing well under the valorous leadership of Vasco Núñez. Why send for a man who had done nothing to help build the village?

The majority of the colonists, however, desiring a peaceful end to the strife over authority, agreed to send an invitation to Nicuesa when and wherever he should be found. They were greatly influenced by the promise of provisions and clothing from Rodrigo de Colmenares should they agree to submit themselves to the leadership of his friend Nicuesa.

"If you are colonists of Nicuesa, these provisions and reinforcements are yours," declared Colmenares beguilingly. "If not, you have no right to them, for they are meant for Nicuesa's men."

Altogether, the bait was too alluring to resist. The colonists voted in favor of Nicuesa.

Three men were selected to accompany Rodrigo de Colmenares as ambassadors from the Darien colony. They were Francisco de Agueros, Diego Albitez and the bachelor of laws, Diego del Corral, who found the wind apparently favoring Nicuesa and immediately deserted his former friend Enciso.

Enciso was further annoyed when the colonists ruled that the brigantine he had built at his own expense was to be used by Rodrigo de Colmenares to make the journey, along with the larger ship of Colmenares.

He could do nothing more than expostulate about the matter, however, and that only to a few friends, for if Nicuesa was to return as governor it would not be well to express too much opposition. Enciso experienced some slight pleasure upon seeing that Balboa was equally ill-pleased. At least, he thought gloatingly, Diego de Nicuesa's arrival would mean the end of the wretched stowaway's climb to power.

As usual, Balboa decided to overcome his mental unrest through physical action. As soon as the two ships had sailed, he headed a party into the interior in search of gold. He was away for some time, returning just as the smaller of the two ships, bearing the three deputies, dropped anchor in the harbor.

Diego del Corral immediately asked all the colonists to assemble in the plaza. When all were waiting to hear his words, he spoke, answering their eager questions.

"Yes," he declared, "we found Diego de Nicuesa."

The men began to cheer at this news, but something in the tone of the speaker silenced them.

Corral continued gloomily. "But the Nicuesa of old is not the Nicuesa of today. Extreme hardship and near starvation have sown cruelty and greed where grace and generosity once abounded. I swear that never have I seen a man so changed, both without and within."

He went on to tell the amazed listeners of the horrible condition in which they had found Diego de Nicuesa. Physically he was mere skin and bones, as were his men who still remained alive. Only sixty men of the original seven hundred survived. Like his contemporary, Ojeda, Nicuesa had failed miserably in the task of colonization. Courtly accomplishments and musical skill were of little use in facing the stern reality of jungle existence.

"They lived," Corral reported, "on roots and lizards. Savages constantly menaced them, so that they dared not stray far from camp in search of more nourishing food. And their commander, instead of becoming more compassionate with these cavaliers whom he had led into such a situation, became unjust and cruel of conduct."

Diego Albitez, another of the deputies sent with Colmenares, nodded. "One of his men, who rescued him from a desert island, received only curses for his aid, for Nicuesa believed he had wilfully delayed to come to him. This soldier we found chained to a palm tree, tattered and even thinner than the others."

Francisco de Agueros nodded. "I spoke to him myself when Nicuesa was not near. His name is Lope de Olano and he is from Biscay."

A cry went up from Martín Zamudio. "Lope de Olano! Why, he is my good friend of childhood. We are distantly related, indeed. Are you sure? Was it that very Lope de Olano?"

Nicuesa's soldiers most in need of care had been sent ahead to Darien along with the deputies, and these men did not hesitate to confirm all that had been told.

Martín Zamudio was indignant. Other Biscayans in the company shared his indignation, for despite the fact that Spain was a united country, each section had its own customs and traditions and was intensely patriotic. Those from Biscay or Catalonia were extremely loyal to one another. Led by the headstrong Martín Zamudio their anger rose dangerously.

Corral lifted his hand to still the crowd.

"But this is not all. No sooner had Nicuesa's extreme hunger been assuaged at a great feast aboard ship than Colmenares spoke of our settlement at Darien and the — er — disagreements here. When Nicuesa heard of the gold that the colonists had gained, he flew into a violent rage."

"But why?" demanded Balboa, stepping forward.

"He declared that the colonists had no right to the gold, since it was found upon his territory and that he meant to get it all back as soon as he reached here."

At this news, the murmurings of discontent in the company rose to a roar. What treasure they possessed had been won with difficulty and they meant to keep it. What right had this half-mad Nicuesa — who had failed in establishing a colony himself — to seize what he had not earned, even though it might be upon his territory?

Vasco Núñez clenched his fists until they ached. His mouth was a long hard line above his firm jawline and his blue eyes burned.

"What we have earned by our labors, by the sweat of our brows, by long perilous trips inland, by battle and by barter — that belongs to us!" he shouted.

The colonists roared approval of this speech.

Martín Zamudio faced the gathering, his mouth working angrily.

"Who is this Nicuesa that he should speak thus of men who have succeeded in colonization where he failed? What sort of leader would he make us? We need men in this land, not guitar-playing courtiers."

"Aye," shouted Fernando Múñoz. "If he should come here, the touch of his fingers would doubtless send our colony crumbling like his own."

Corral stood somewhat taken aback by the tumult he had caused. He had meant to warn the colonists, not to incite them to open rebellion.

He lifted a hand in an attempt to get their attention once more, but soon saw that it was impossible. The men were milling around in disorder, shouting, knotting into vehement groups. The largest gathering, Corral saw with foreboding, was listening to Vasco Núñez de Balboa who was speaking decisively. Corral shrugged and shouldered his way out of the crowd, evading Enciso who apparently wanted to talk with him further. Diego de Corral had bellowed himself into a headache and at the moment wanted only to reach the blessed seclusion of his own cabin.

"Where is Nicuesa now?" asked Juan de Valdivia of one of the deputies.

"He has delayed in coming, in order that he may capture some native slaves and bring them with him."

Juan de Valdivia spoke grimly. "That delay may cost him much, if I am any judge of the trend of things." He indicated the crowd. "They are not worms, you know — as the overthrow of Enciso's unbearable government has shown."

A few days later, a messenger from Nicuesa arrived in a small boat. He was Juan de Caicedo. His reception was sullen.

"I have been asked to tell you that Diego de Nicuesa will arrive not later than day after tomorrow."

The Darien colonists received this information by glowering.

Juan de Caicedo, haggard from his life of misfortune and privation with Nicuesa, looked from one to another of the men searchingly. In each face he saw discontent. Some were evidently rebellious; others received the news with brooding resignation; others did not meet his gaze, but looked stoically out over the ocean. On no face did he see a welcome for his ruthless master, Diego de Nicuesa.

"Oh, what fools you are!" he burst out savagely.

Every eye turned toward him in surprise.

"You are your own masters now," continued Caicedo. "Your gold is your own — your lives are your own. You are doing far better by yourselves than ever we fared with Nicuesa as leader. And yet, in your pitiful stupidity, you actually invite an oppressor to rule you!"

Such a speech from the messenger of Nicuesa himself, spoken with a force and sincerity that could not be doubted, threw the colonists into even deeper despair. All their worst forebodings were confirmed. But what to do about the matter? The invitation had been sent to Nicuesa. He was on his way.

"We are doomed," said Bartolomé Hurtado. Viciously he kicked a stone from his path.

Balboa, walking beside him, furrows of concentration in his sun-browned forehead, appeared not to have heard. After several minutes of silence, he slapped his friend on the shoulder.

"I have it!" His voice was strong with resolution.

Bartolomé winced from the slap. "You have *what*?" he asked somberly.

"The solution to this Nicuesa business!"

Bartolomé stopped short, his eyes alight. "You have? What?"

He gripped Balboa's arm. "Come! Let's have the ray of hope. 'Tis greatly needed — and if practical, Vasco Núñez, so much the better!"

"Hold, Bartolomé, let's call the rest of our comrades — and put the plan before them all."

With the men surrounding him in a receptive but none too optimistic mood, Balboa spoke. His voice was vibrant and his words convincing.

"You are all agreed that Nicuesa's coming would be fatal to the best interests of our colony?"

All shouted assent.

"And you are all agreed that your invitation to him was a great mistake?"

"Aye. Aye. A terrible blunder!"

"Then," said Balboa, his eyes sweeping the countenances lifted to his, "your remedy is simple. When he arrives, refuse to permit him to land."

There was startled quiet, then a great roar of approval went up. Of course! That was it. Why had no one thought of it before? Ah, this Vasco Núñez de Balboa — he was a match for every adverse circumstance. A leader in a million!

Each swore not to bow to Nicuesa's rule, to prevent his disembarking when he arrived. With grim determination, but more optimistic now, they awaited the coming of Nicuesa's ship.

CHAPTER XIV

PLOTS AND COUNTERPLOTS

THE STRAIN OF WAITING FOR NICUESA BECAME INTOLERABLE. DAYS
passed, burning with the jungle heat and the passions of Zamudio and his following of Biscayans.

Common talk was that these men had secretly conspired to
slay the new governor immediately upon his arrival. They
would meet the ship in force, it was said, go aboard it and spike
the body of Nicuesa to the deck with their halberds. With a
blood oath they had sworn vengeance upon him for the horrible
treatment of Lope de Olano, and nothing upon earth could
move them to change their minds.

Vasco Núñez had no reason to doubt that this rumor was
true. Each day he had watched Zamudio and his friends go
silently into the woods. Here they made their plans, he knew,
while parrots squawked raucously overhead and the steaming
breath of the great inland swamps rose about them. For hours
at a time they would remain away from the settlement, hidden
from view.

Their return was always marked by slow, measured steps,
and sulky demeanors. Though their faces were swollen from
mosquito bites and their shoes clogged with mud, they seemed
not to care. Nor would they discuss with the other colonists
where they had gone or what had been said at their meetings.
Of these matters, Zamudio, when pressed, would merely answer, waving his hand deprecatingly: "I know not. Ask the
others."

Upon the evening before the expected arrival of Nicuesa's caravel, Vasco Núñez decided that, in the interests of all the colonists, it would be wise to summon the Biscayans to his own house to talk things over. If the followers of Zamudio really intended to carry out their grim plan, something must be done about it. The murder of a man given the king's authority in the form of a royal grant to colonize these lands was bad business. Even though he might be the worst of tyrants, as he apparently was, the crown would hardly condone such action. Eventually they would all be punished — perhaps hanged.

Any man whose vision was not blurred by headlong passion ought to see that under no circumstances would it be advisable to incur the displeasure of Ferdinand. This was a Spanish colony and they were all Spaniards first and last, not merely Biscayans or Catalonians, or natives of some other district, as the case might be. Their sovereign came first and would always come first here in Terra Firma as well as in the old land.

Balboa tried to explain this to Zamudio.

"Slay this Nicuesa," he said, "and we may ourselves be slain."

Zamudio was stubborn. "The king would not ask that a madman be placed over us."

"Perhaps not. But first His Majesty must be acquainted with the fact that Nicuesa is mad."

"By that time it would be too late to save the victims of his wrath," Zamudio argued.

Silence fell in the room as Balboa paced across and back, his flaming hair uncovered, his eyes darkening with thought. Suddenly he paused, his voice persuasive:

"Surely I have already pointed out to you a more reasonable course than that you contemplate. Let him come, but do not let him land — "

" 'Tis a treatment too gentle for such a fiend!" Zamudio spoke fiercely.

The others reaffirmed what their leader had said by nodding their heads sullenly.

Balboa used all his eloquence, pleading with them to be fair-minded and reasonable, begging them not to use violence.

"He who uses violence cannot himself escape the deadly fumes of it."

Hours later when the Biscayans filed out, Balboa was by no means sure that he had even dented their grim determination. But he had tried. No man could do more.

Nicuesa arrived the next morning. His caravel sailed up the harbor and anchored off shore. Vasco Núñez watched a lean form with hawklike face come forward and stand by the rail.

Orders rang out to lower the boats. But before the lines tightened to raise them from the deck, Zamudio's voice struck into the tense quiet, heavy and resounding.

"Stand where you are, Diego de Nicuesa, upon penalty of death!"

Startled, the lean figure straightened, scanning the curving shore line and the crowd gathered there. Not an eye flinched. Everywhere he looked were grim, unfriendly faces. No one spoke a word. This was a far cry from the enthusiastic reception Nicuesa had expected. Muscular, heavy-bearded men stood shoulder to shoulder in an implied command more deadly, though silent, than that which had been thundered by Zamudio.

Vasco Núñez reluctantly felt pity stirring within him. True, by his own selfishness Nicuesa had brought this upon himself, yet he had survived great sufferings and privations. Even from a distance, his emaciation was apparent. Balboa could see the tightness of skin over protruding bones. Eyes dulled with fever were opening and closing as if trying to brush away the film of unreality. His head moved uncertainly from side to side, as if trying to find an anchor for his reason.

He said sharply: "I am your new governor. Launch the boat!"

No one heard him. At least, there was no motion aboard the caravel to obey. The crowd had become threatening. Here and there an arm lifted in defiance. Coarse shouts arose.

Balboa stepped forward upon the wet beach sand, a silhouette against the blaze of sun upon the water.

"These men are determined that you must not come ashore," he called to Nicuesa. "They feel that they have earned the right to say who shall govern them."

Anger rocked Nicuesa's figure. "Are you that notorious flame-headed Vasco Núñez de Balboa?"

"Aye, sir."

"I have heard of you — an upstart, a debtor, a stowaway, an impudent, loud-talking no-account —"

"Hold your peace!" Zamudio shouted. "It is you, not he, who is to be judged. And the judgment won't be to your liking!"

Nicuesa's already frail form seemed to diminish.

"What would you have of me?" he faltered finally.

"We would have none of you," cried Zamudio. He waded out into the water and shook his fist. "You cannot stay here. There is no place for such as you in Terra Firma. You must depart hence — and quickly, too."

"Depart! But — where?"

"We care not."

"But I crave that you permit me and my men to come ashore. I pray that you allow me to plead my case."

Another man on the ship's deck came forward to stand beside Nicuesa. Balboa recognized Rodrigo de Colmenares whom, until now, he had forgotten.

"Aye, men of Darien," cried Colmenares, "be reasonable. Let Diego de Nicuesa come ashore. Among you there, I see the very deputies who brought him the invitation. Do you now retract it without an explanation?"

The crowd grumbled uncertainly.

"Aye, permit me that one favor — to plead my case before you all," pleaded the unhappy Nicuesa.

Balboa stepped forward. " 'Tis only just," he said. "What harm can result from permitting him to land and speak to us? Our men outnumber his by far. We cannot condemn a man without a hearing."

Although Zamudio and his followers grumbled and Enciso and Corral whined disapproval, it was at length agreed that Nicuesa should be allowed to plead his case at a public meeting the following day.

Next morning an escort went out to meet him and accompanied him and his men to the plaza. All the colonists were assembled there, rough men for the most part, tanned almost black by the sun, hardened by exposure and every kind of hardship; men who had faced death for gold, who had measured their strength against the pitiless savagery of the jungle. Of such was the assembly that had grudgingly consented to give Diego de Nicuesa a hearing. They listened, but it was obvious from the start that each man had already decided what his verdict would be. They heard his words politely, but unmoved.

When his speech ended, a low murmur went forth. Enciso, knowing that a decision in favor of Nicuesa would destroy forever his claim to the rule, shrugged his shoulders and turned away.

Not desiring to influence anyone, either by sign or word, Balboa also drew apart from the crowd. Zamudio, however, pressed forward. He stood close to Nicuesa now and raised his hand for silence.

"Our decision," he said, in an oddly throaty voice, "remains unaltered. No one wants you here, Diego de Nicuesa. You must go."

"Aye!" shouted the crowd.

When his voice could be heard, Nicuesa made a final plea which moved many, if not to support him, at least to sympathize with him. He was a broken man, he said. Perhaps they were right in believing that he would fail as governor. Yet he had so much at stake. Already he had spent a fortune in supplies and ships. Disaster following disaster had driven him almost mad with despair. Somehow he must recover at least a part of the money he had lost. In fairness, wouldn't they, the colonists of Darien, permit him to join them? He would accept even the humble post of foot soldier. He would do anything they told him if only they would give him this last chance to share in the treasure taken in Terra Firma.

His voice trembled to a full stop. His eyes, sunken into the wrinkled darkness of his skin, shifted pleadingly from face to face. He lifted shaking hands to touch the dryness of his lips.

Once more a murmur broke among the assembly. Many, including Balboa, were in favor of accepting Nicuesa's last request. Surely, in all humanity, they could not reject such a simple petition from a man to whom the king had granted the very soil on which they stood.

However, it was plain that Zamudio and the other Biscayans felt no compassion. They set up such a hue and cry against Nicuesa that presently many more were won over to their side.

Zamudio insisted that if Nicuesa became one of them, even

in the capacity of foot soldier, he would soon spread discontent and take every chance offered to improve his position. Neither was he physically fit to bear arms, nor likely to be amenable to discipline. No, it would never do. Better to send him away now, than to regret it later.

"You must go," Zamudio told Nicuesa firmly.

Francisco Benítez, one of the Biscayans, strode over to where Nicuesa stood cowering before that noisy throng. To the amazement of all, he spat upon him, cursing him with foul words.

Enraged, Balboa leapt forward. With one quick motion, he seized Benítez and summoned two foot soldiers.

"Take this shameless bully and give him ten strokes of the lash!"

Swearing vengeance, Benítez was dragged away.

The behavior of the crowd did not improve, however, but became more ominous. A riot was imminent. To save Nicuesa from further embarrassment and probable physical injury or even death, Balboa escorted him back to the ship.

"Stay here," he commanded, "else I cannot be responsible."

Not until the next day did Balboa learn of Nicuesa's fate. Secretly the Biscayans and a few other colonists headed by Zamudio had gone down to the beach under cover of darkness. Inviting Nicuesa ashore on the pretext they wished to parley with him further, they soon had him gagged and bound, a prisoner.

"Now," said Zamudio, "you shall listen to us. A ship is ready to take you to Santo Domingo. Refuse and you shall be slain right here."

Nicuesa, having no alternative, went. The old ship to which he was conveyed was not the fine caravel aboard which he had sailed so proudly into the harbor. It was a vessel so unseaworthy that it had been restricted to very short voyages up and down the coast. It leaked and its bottom had been riddled by ship's worms. Though the winds favored and the sea was calm, there was not one chance in a thousand that Nicuesa and his seventeen loyal followers could ever arrive safely at their destination.

"Show thy face, O Lord," Nicuesa had cried as the vessel moved out of the harbor, "and we shall be saved."

Aghast at what the conspirators had done, Balboa hurriedly called them together and publicly denounced their act.

"It would have been more humane," he concluded, "to have slain him with your swords, also the seventeen brave men who refused to desert him."

Zamudio only laughed. With unrelenting hearts he and his followers dispersed and went about their business. The last to go was Francisco Benítez, the man whom Balboa had ordered lashed. Shuffling along behind the others, he suddenly turned and directed toward Balboa a look that could not be misinterpreted.

"Watch out," that baleful glance told him, "or you, too, may suffer an even worse fate than Diego de Nicuesa!"

CHAPTER XV

A DECISION FOR THE KING

THESE WERE TROUBLED DAYS FOR BALBOA. NO SOONER HAD ONE emergency passed than another presented itself. The business of Nicuesa had been disposed of only to bring the problem of the lawyer Enciso into the foreground again.

Who was really the leader of the colonists at this time no one could be certain. Balboa and Zamudio had been elected. Each one had a certain authority. Each chose to exercise it in his own way. As a result a number of factions arose: those favoring Zamudio and his methods, those favoring Balboa, those favoring Enciso, and those favoring nobody. The little colony was moving with dangerous speed toward destruction. Everybody wanted to rule. Nobody wanted to obey. No one was satisfied.

Least of all Enciso. The summary dispatching of his rival, Diego de Nicuesa, secretly pleased him. The action had been Zamudio's, but the wily lawyer preferred to consider it the work of a man he feared more, Balboa. He sensed, or perhaps knew, that in Vasco Núñez de Balboa were many qualities which pre-eminently fitted him to become one of Spain's greatest conquistadors. He had courage, imagination, and initiative of a high order. His prowess as a soldier was already so well known that whenever an occasion for battle arose, the expedition immediately turned to him for leadership. His judgment, too, had proved good. No treasure would have been taken by them from Terra Firma, except for Balboa. Neither could they have established themselves so firmly here in Darien without him. Every good fortune that had come to them had somehow been speeded by his hand.

For his own part, Balboa saw in Enciso an obstacle to progress. Enciso was a calculating, self-centered man who would sacrifice everybody to his own ambition. Zamudio, on the other hand, though far too impulsive and passionate, too often unreasonable, had not a selfish streak in him. He might err, as he had done in Nicuesa's case, but he had erred in the honest belief that what he was doing would be to the advantage of all. Unlike Enciso, he neither resented Balboa's abilities nor was jealous of him. They were, in spite of a difference of opinion, good friends.

One thing that both Balboa and Zamudio had in common was distrust of Enciso. Both realized that so long as he remained in the settlement there could be no peace. Nor were they wrong in this. Soon after the departure of Nicuesa, the puffy figure of Enciso could be seen going from cabin to cabin pleading his cause. Gathering a few trusted lieutenants about him, he made an impassioned speech demanding the overthrow of Balboa and Zamudio.

"Much gold and great power will be yours," he promised, "if you will only aid me in undermining the power of those two rascals."

In a few days Enciso's plots were hatching in most unexpected quarters. Those of the colony who had been shocked by the treatment meted out to Nicuesa, rallied to the support of their former leader. Men who for various reasons had been reprimanded or punished by Balboa, such as the insolent Francisco Benítez, also joined him. In less than a week Enciso, by means of his persuasive lies and half-truths, had become almost as powerful as the two alcaldes. At this rate, Balboa perceived, the colonists would soon be back where they were when Enciso had begun to make his numerous hurtful laws.

One afternoon Zamudio came to Balboa in a highly excited state, insisting that they arrest Enciso immediately.

"If not," he declared, "we are lost. The whole expedition will be ruined. He is gathering followers at a rate that amazes me."

"He has a very eloquent tongue," Balboa said.

"Then let him use it in his own defense," stormed Zamudio. "We will arrest him and put him on trial."

"With what specific crime shall he be charged?" asked Balboa.

"Conspiracy."

"He will claim that we, instead, are the conspirators." Balboa shrugged.

Zamudio strode up and down the room, mopping his brow and blowing out his breath. Now and again, he stopped short, snorting, then furiously began to pace again.

"Think! Think, man!" he presently cried.

"I am thinking," said Balboa quietly.

Zamudio's red face grew redder and his black beard bristled. "Has this man broken no law then?"

Balboa considered this, then spoke slowly. "Well, he has usurped power by acting as Ojeda's representative in territory belonging to Nicuesa."

"But are we not guilty of the same offense?"

"Aye," sighed Balboa, "I fear so."

"Then what shall we do about it? I insist we do something before it is too late." He thumped his fist on the table. "You know as well as I do what will happen if Enciso takes over again. We shall be bound like worms in the cocoon of his law-making."

"I know."

It was a problem that challenged even the ingenuity of Balboa. He took the night to think it over. Lying in his hammock with the friendly tropical stars peeping through his window, with the silence drawn about him like a comforting cloak, he could always think better. His was the kind of spirit that could draw inspiration from elemental things, from the sun shining on water, from the wind stirring the palms, from green grass and forests and the shining peaks of faraway mountains.

Tonight, as he stretched out, there came to him the thought that the forthright way was generally the better one. Enciso indeed had his claim to authority just as he and Zamudio had. It became clear to him then that neither side could rightly judge the claims of the other. Truly, it was a matter for the crown, for King Ferdinand himself to decide. Yes, that was the solution. They must dispatch a ship to Spain. Enciso should go and Zamudio, too. Each would make his plea before the king, and the king could decide between them.

Having decided, Balboa slept soundly. He woke late to hear, from the direction of the plaza, voices raised in dispute, soldiers marching in step, dogs barking, men shouting.

Dressing hurriedly, he ran to the public square, Leonçico bounding beside him.

"What is the cause of all this commotion?" he demanded of a foot soldier.

The man looked surprised. "Certainly you know. Enciso has been arrested and thrown into jail." He laughed boisterously. "It is that same jail he built so carefully to harbor other offenders! A fine joke, eh?"

Once more Zamudio had impulsively taken matters into his own hands. At first Balboa was angry and would have reproached his fellow alcalde. But on second thought it seemed better not to. In a few more days Enciso's conspiracy would have come to a head and he might have usurped the authority now held by himself and Zamudio. No, for the present, at least, jail would be a good place for him. It would be difficult for him to conduct his intrigues from there. The trial would be a farce, of course, but it would amuse the colonists and might put some proper humility into Enciso.

At the trial a week later the prisoner was declared guilty of founding a colony on land belonging to another. His goods and property were taken from him. His gold was confiscated. He was made to realize that the machinery of the law which he so dearly loved to set in motion could grind in its cogs lawyers as well as laymen. For once he had his full of it, choking on the very phrases he himself had often mouthed with such pleasure. He clamored to be out of jail, threatening revenge.

Balboa let him cool a week. The voice that had clamored incessantly from the jail the first day or two grew quieter. The prisoner's barks became growls, and growls, whines. Enciso's tone grew conciliatory. He called out to anyone who might be passing his log prison that if his property were returned to him, he'd be willing to listen to reason. His expert pleading began to have its effect on the colonists. Instead of pausing before the dark cage to taunt its occupant, they now hurried by with averted faces, feeling a little guilty.

Now was the opportune time for Balboa to present his plan of submitting the case to King Ferdinand.

Enciso was jubilant. Certainly he would go. His eyes lighted shrewdly and Balboa guessed that he was thinking of the speech he would make before the Spanish court. An eloquent appeal, no doubt, with dark allusions to his rivals — quick passages of wit and sarcasm, thundering condemnations. For even better than he loved to make laws Enciso loved to make

speeches, and he would gladly journey all the way to Spain
to do it.

Against such eloquence Zamudio would have nothing to offer
except a deep sincerity and a certain rugged philosophy in all
that he said. He was no match for Enciso as an orator, Balboa
knew, but surely the eyes of the king and court would see behind the wily artifices of the lawyer. They would know him
for what he was, a man obsessed with delusions of grandeur,
a scheming pettifogger.

Zamudio readily fell in with the plan. He had a family back
in Biscay and the idea of an audience with King Ferdinand
himself impressed him. He felt that it was evidence of his
progress in the world. What prestige it would give him with
his stay-at-home friends back in Spain! He promised Balboa
to do everything possible, not only to discredit Enciso, but to
secure the king's aid in procuring more supplies and men for
the struggling Darien colony.

The matter settled, Balboa next summoned his most loyal
friend in Darien, the nobleman Juan de Valdivia. He had still
another trump card to play.

From a strongbox in his room he brought forth a sack of
gold, part of his own share in the expedition. Smiling, he gave
it to Juan.

"I desire that you accompany Zamudio and Enciso when the
ship sails tomorrow," he said. "At Santo Domingo, enroute to
Spain, you will disembark and proceed at once to the governor
of Española, Don Diego Columbus."

"Aye," nodded Valdivia wonderingly.

"This gold is a gift to the governor and the royal treasurer,
Miguel de Pasamonte."

Juan de Valdivia's eyes opened wide with understanding.

"Pasamonte is a favorite of the king," he said, "and young

Columbus is a worthy son of the great admiral. Your reasoning is perfect, Vasco Núñez."

Balboa laughed. "We need the influence they have with the king. In return for this little gift, seek supplies and soldiers for our settlement."

"That I will do."

"More important still," Balboa continued, "secure from these worthy men some recognition of our claims. We need official sanction. Our authority must be recognized or else —" he shrugged expressively.

Valdivia threw his arms around his troubled friend and embraced him.

"For a man so courageous and so right," he declared, "I am prepared to do my utmost. Fear not that in any way I shall fail you."

"I have no fear," Balboa said affectionately. "You are a true friend, Juan de Valdivia."

CHAPTER XVI

NEWS OF TWO SPANISH DESERTERS

BALBOA WAS WELL AWARE OF THE BEST WAY HE COULD PROVE HIS worth as Governor of Darien to King Ferdinand. Gold was the answer. The more treasure he could remit to the Spanish court, he believed, the more favorable would his situation be.

From time to time he had received reports of a wealthy Indian province called Coyba, about thirty leagues distant. There, according to various captured Indians, were fabulous riches — gold, pearls, precious stones and metals of all kinds.

His imagination was fired by these tall tales of splendor. He determined to send a party to explore the province. Looking around for a likely leader, his eye fell on Francisco Pizarro. He summoned him to the cabildo with six other soldiers and unfolded his plan. They listened eagerly.

Pizarro's eyes were bright in his lean eaglelike countenance.

"There is nothing I would like better than to lead a company to Coyba."

Balboa nodded approval at this hardy speech.

"You will start tomorrow, following the course of the river Darien." He gave them further instructions, supplied them with trade goods, trinkets, hawk bells, inexpensive jewelry.

"Gain the goodwill of the Indians, whose countries you traverse," he told them. "Kindness makes friends; fear, only enemies." Seeing the skepticism in the eyes of Pizarro, he emphasized sternly: "Use your weapons only if necessary for defense."

The next day the scouting party started out, cheered on their way by the colonists, some envious that they had not been chosen to go.

Balboa himself watched them with wistful eyes as they disappeared among the palms and tangling vines of the jungle. He had wanted desperately to go himself, but there were more important things to do in the settlement. The task of governing this restless band of Spanish adventurers was by no means an easy one. Even with Enciso gone, many of his adherents remained, stirring up dissatisfaction with Balboa's rule whenever they could. To govern firmly but fairly — what a problem that was!

He sighed, reached down to pat Leonçico's head, and turned back to his cabin. It was a gloomy day. The sun, appearing briefly, had soon been overwhelmed by swiftly gathering clouds. It was warm and suffocating in the valley settlement. In the closeness of his cabin, perspiration bathed his body. His beard was wet and moisture ran into his eyes, blurring his vision. He felt constrained in this swampy lowland country, for he had been born and reared in the rugged Province of Estremadura. The beckoning crags of the far mountains continually allured him. He longed to breathe once more the clear sharp air of the heights. He wiped his forehead with one great palm and pushed his fingers impatiently through his hair.

"You said you wished to see me?"

Vasco Núñez looked up. Rodrigo de Colmenares stood in the doorway, his tall figure shutting even the gray half-light from the room.

"Ah, yes, I'd almost forgotten. Come in, Colmenares. It was about Nicuesa's men that I wanted to see you. Those that were left at Nombre de Dios. They fare badly, I hear."

"Very badly," Colmenares nodded, seating himself and leaning forward. "Despite the food that has been sent several times to them from Darien, they are perishing at the rate of five and six a day from exposure, illness, and Indian raids."

"And nothing has been heard of Nicuesa," said Balboa slowly, shaking his head.

"Nothing." Colmenares' voice was resentful. "Nor is it to be expected that anything will be heard, driven away as he was in that most unseaworthy of vessels."

"No one regrets that occurrence more than I," said Balboa. "I have told you time and again that it was done without my knowledge or consent."

"I know. 'Twas the work of Zamudio. Still —"

"Nicuesa, nevertheless, was surely unfit for the leadership of our colony. His own men testified loudest against him, as you well know."

"Aye, and yet he was my personal friend and a gallant one before his soul was warped by his bitter adversities. His likely fate sits heavily upon my heart." Colmenares' eyes stared through the window.

Balboa's eyes followed his. A breeze was stirring now, strengthening minute by minute, breaking the morning's unnatural quiet. Palm leaves moved, increasingly agitated. In the fields beyond the village, the silken grain bowed and rippled.

"A storm is coming." His lips were grim. "I had hoped that it would miss us."

Colmenares nodded. "The crops."

"Aye, these violent windy cloudbursts make great havoc with our food supplies." He shrugged. "Well, about the survivors at Nombre de Dios. Something must be done for them."

"I am agreed."

"There's only one thing to do. Send a ship and bring them back here." He frowned. Provisions were none too plentiful now. After this storm, there would be less. These weak, failing men of Nicuesa would add to the burden. Yet, as a Christian, could he do less than succor them?

Rodrigo de Colmenares rose, his hand extended.

"Yours is a generous heart, Vasco Núñez de Balboa. If ever I doubted the worth of your character, those doubts are withdrawn. Count me henceforth as a loyal follower."

"I should rather count you as a friendly counselor. I am in need of such."

Outside the wind and rain struck, with a fury as of some personal vengeance. The crash and roar of it muffled the answering words of Rodrigo de Colmenares, but his smile in the dim light warmed Balboa's heart. What is better and more heartening to a man who delights in friendship than gaining a new friend?

The next day Colmenares embarked for his voyage to Nombre de Dios.

Scarcely had he departed, when Francisco Pizarro's men came staggering back to the settlement, bleeding and crippled from sore wounds. Their weak hails and agonized groans brought the colonists out of their cabins, aghast.

Balboa ran forward to assist one of the most seriously hurt.

"What happened?"

Francisco Pizarro told them briefly. Scarcely three leagues from Darien they had been set upon by Indians led by the cacique, Cemaco, he whom the colonists had driven from this very village. Although greatly outnumbered, the Spaniards had rushed into the thick of the foe. Many natives were slain and the rest fled, but Pizarro, fearing another assault, had retreated immediately.

Balboa's eyes raked the men. One was missing. Francisco Hernan.

"Where is he?" he demanded. "Slain?"

Pizarro's eyes dropped. "Not slain, but greatly disabled. Unable to retreat with us. We had not time to — "

Anger flamed in Balboa's eyes. "Not time to rescue a comrade, Pizarro?"

"We feared another attack momentarily. I thought it not wise to — " His face paled and one hand went to a wounded shoulder where red stained a crude bandage.

"For shame, Francisco Pizarro!" Balboa's voice shook with indignation. "Shall it be said of Spaniards and Christians that they abandon a comrade for fear of infidels?"

Pizarro gnawed his lip. He saw the indignation flaring through others.

"I will return," he said, "and bring Francisco Hernan back."

Despite his wound, he was true to his word. Francisco Hernan was rescued and brought back to the village and eventually he recovered.

Rodrigo de Colmenares, returning with the grateful men from Nombre de Dios, brought with him a story that was to be of great significance in the life of Vasco Núñez de Balboa.

Somewhere along the Isthmus, Colmenares and his men had gone ashore for water. Two naked savages had appeared suddenly, shouting to them in perfect Castilian. They proved to be Spaniards who had deserted from Nicuesa a year and a half before. An Indian ruler of the province of Coyba had received them hospitably. This cacique, Careta by name, had saved them from starvation by his kindness. They had been given native wives and dwellings. These Indian lands, they had informed Colmenares, were rich in both grain and gold.

One of the two Spaniards, Juan Alonzo, had returned to Darien with him, Colmenares said.

"Juan Alonzo, step forward," said Balboa.

He questioned the man at length concerning the wealth of the cacique Careta. The need of the Darien colonists for more food was becoming desperate. Storms had flattened the crops. Moreover, it appeared that King Ferdinand's royal fifth would be anything but impressive if more gold was not secured immediately.

"Juan Alonzo," he said, "where is your companion?"

"He returned to Careta's village," said the soldier. He looked at Rodrigo de Colmenares, who nodded encouragement. "It was decided best, in the event that you might desire to send an expedition to Coyba for supplies. He would be of value there, he thought."

Balboa clapped Alonzo approvingly on the shoulder.

"He thought wisely," he said. "For that is exactly what we are going to do. Grain and gold — we need both sorely."

The colonists cheered heartily, enthusiastic over the prospect of both food and treasure. Excited, too, at the prospect of exploration, for they were all adventurous cavaliers.

Balboa, starting for a meeting with Bartolomé Hurtado and Rodrigo de Colmenares, turned back as an afterthought.

"I don't believe I heard the name of your companion, Juan Alonzo."

The soldier respectfully detached himself from the clamoring group around him.

"He is called Andrés Garavito," he said.

CHAPTER XVII

IN CARETA'S VILLAGE

ANCHORING HIS TWO BRIGANTINES OFF THE COAST OF THE INDIAN province of Coyba, Balboa led his men to the village of the cacique, Careta.

Contrary to the expectation of the Spaniards, who had expected armed opposition, the Indian ruler received them with cordial dignity.

Balboa was astonished. Careta hardly conformed to the popular Spanish conception of a savage. Indeed, his bearing was royal, his manner courteous, his speech gentle and refined. Tall and well-built, he walked with an easy grace to meet them.

"Greetings, strangers from afar. Welcome to the dominions of Coyba." His brown eyes met Balboa's confidently, and without a trace of fear. Gold bracelets gleamed on his arms as he raised them in native greeting. On his head was an elaborate headdress of woven feathers.

Careta escorted the soldiers into the village. Here, the inhabitants gathered around them curiously. Naked brown children ran to meet them, offering bright plumes and exotic tropical flowers. Maidens, the fairest Balboa had ever seen in Terra Firma, chanted melodious greetings.

In the cacique's pavilion, Andrés Garavito came toward them. At first glance, Balboa took him for one of the natives. He was nearly naked and wore colored parrot feathers and Indian ornaments.

"Andrés!" He embraced him affectionately. "After so long a time, we meet again — and how fortunately!"

"Aye, fortunately indeed." Andrés Garavito stood back and appraised Balboa, his eyes slanting questions. "You have done well, I hear."

"Aye, very well." Bartolomé Hurtado stepped forward. "Our old friend is now ruler of the Darien colony."

"So? I congratulate you. I had not thought your farming in Isla Española would ever lead to anything, I'll admit. But if it led to this prominence, Vasco Núñez — "

"Indirectly," responded Balboa, smiling broadly, "it did, Andrés. But the road was rocky and exceedingly roundabout. Later, perhaps, I shall explain more clearly. But now, we have other matters more important to consider."

He turned to the cacique, who waited benevolently, and followed him to one end of the room where the ruler's family waited. There were four young braves, handsome and well-proportioned and fully as poised as their father. Balboa was much impressed by these youths, but his eyes lingered upon Careta's only daughter. He had never seen a maid so fair. Her shining hair fell raven-black to her smooth golden shoulders. Her eyes were deep and velvet-dark under her lashes. Her features were as delicate as those of any highbred Castilian lady.

Balboa took a deep breath and bowed over her hand which lay in his great one like a trembling prisoned bird.

"I greet you in the manner of my country," he said, "and with all the admiration due your beauty."

"I am humbled at your favor," she said and the low native tongue was as music in his ears.

Vasco Núñez turned. Andrés Garavito stood a little behind him, staring at the princess. Balboa looked back at the maid and saw that she, too, had become conscious of Andrés' gaze, and had turned her head away from him disdainfully.

Careta spoke at his side. "For what reason do you honor our province with this visit, revered stranger?"

Startled, Balboa blurted his mission: "We have come for food and gold, for we have been told both are abundant here in Coyba."

There was a short silence. Careta's face remained expressionless. Then he spoke slowly.

"At another time, I should be glad to grant your request. I have never denied food and rest to anyone in need. But now I have barely enough for my own people, for we are at war with the cacique of Ponca and have not been able to cultivate our fields."

Vasco Núñez and his companions received these words despairingly. Those left at Darien had only enough food to last until the return of the expedition from Coyba. They themselves had not sufficient for the homeward voyage. Starvation loomed, a specter no less horrible because of its familiarity. Were they to go through again those ghastly days at San Sebastian, existing like starved wolves instead of human beings?

The voice of Andrés Garavito came softly in Balboa's ear.

"Pretend to believe him. Later I will talk to you again. I have a plan."

Balboa turned to the cacique. "Our people are near starvation. Have you nothing at all to spare? A little maize, yucca for bread — or even some dried flesh of lizards?"

Careta hesitated, then said firmly: "I regret that there is nothing. I can invite those of you here to share our humble meal. That is all."

"Agree," murmured Andrés Garavito persistently. "I will speak to you later."

There was nothing to do but to consent. The Spaniards were given food at one meal and no gold at all. The cacique professed not to have any to trade for the hawk bells, mirrors and trinkets offered by the colonists.

Andrés Garavito, however, asked Balboa for one of the bells to present to the cacique's daughter, the Princess Luaia.

Reluctantly, Balboa gave it to him. He was much heartened to see that she flung it carelessly aside. Garavito's face grew red as potter's clay at this evidence of her disdain.

He strode over to Balboa. "Come to my hut," he said sharply. "I will unfold my plan to you now. I have explained to the cacique that we are old friends and wish to discuss former happenings together before you must leave."

Hoping that Garavito had a knowledge of some place near where they might obtain the coveted provisions, Balboa followed. With him he took Juan Alonzo, Bartolomé Hurtado and Rodrigo de Colmenares.

An Indian woman rose from a corner of the dwelling where she had been grinding meal between two stones. At a curt word from Andrés Garavito, she scurried out, leaving the men alone.

"The cacique lied," said Garavito abruptly.

"Aye." Juan Alonzo nodded vigorously. "He has a secret hoard of provisions, as well as abundant treasure obtained by trading with natives to the south."

"Nevertheless," went on Garavito, "it would be unwise to accuse Careta of this falsehood now. Pretend to believe him and take your leave, as if returning to the ships."

"You mean — ?"

"Aye, it will only be pretense. In the dead of night, when Careta and his people sleep, we shall return and overpower them."

Balboa frowned. "I like it not. We have been hospitably received—"

"You came for supplies to Coyba," said Garavito slyly. "Will you return empty-handed to those at Darien?"

"Nevertheless, I care not for the deceit of your plan. Provisions we need—aye. But I should prefer to do battle honestly. here and now!" He leapt to his feet, hand grasping his sword.

"And I!" Hurtado jumped up as well.

"You will lose twice as many men," said Juan Alonzo reasonably.

"Which do you consider of greater value, Vasco Núñez," asked Garavito, narrow eyes glinting, "infidels or Spaniards?"

"He is right." Colmenares spoke slowly. "The lives of our men are precious. Spare them we must, even though the means be trickery."

"Aye, Vasco Núñez, allow the head to be lord over the heart in this instance," urged Garavito.

Balboa paced the small hut, his thoughts longing to find a nobler solution to the great problem before him. The confines of this little native house were prison-size. Likewise, it seemed, were his better impulses to be bound by their jailer, necessity.

His good judgment revolted at repaying the cacique's hospitality thus. Yet had not Careta lied? And was not the need of the Spaniards extreme? These were his men, their welfare placed in his hands by their own volition. Their lives were at stake. Could he turn them back, despairing, to Darien?

He turned abruptly, his voice rough: "Very well, I will agree to this scheme of yours, Andrés Garavito."

"Ah, 'tis well!" There was triumph glinting in the other's narrow eyes. He licked his full lips.

"But on one condition." Balboa's eyes went round the group sternly. "Do not slay unnecessarily. Rather, take captives.

And not one hair of the cacique or his family must be hurt."

"Agreed!" Colmenares stood up.

Balboa turned to Garavito as the others filed out ahead.

"Tell me, Andrés. Have you no gratitude that you thus conspire to betray the very cacique whose kindness and hospitality saved your life?"

The muscles of Garavito's face jerked, then grew smooth.

"I have more gratitude to Spain and King Ferdinand. I cannot see his Christian subjects starve, while idol worshipers grow fat."

"Well spoken, Andrés!" Balboa put a hand to his shoulder. "Forgive my idle questioning. I respect your loyalty to His Majesty and to glorious Spain."

Andrés Garavito laughed shortly.

"But I have another reason, too, Vasco Núñez."

Stepping into the searing sunlight, Balboa's feet halted, then moved woodenly forward. No hesitation now. The decision was made.

CHAPTER XVIII

BALBOA AND THE PRINCESS

"THE CACIQUE'S FAMILY — ARE THEY ALL SAFE?" BALBOA TURNED to Rodrigo de Colmenares, who had come from Careta's dwelling. The battle had hardly deserved the name, so swift had been the successful overpowering of the sleeping natives. Balboa stood now in the village center, directing his men.

"All but the girl — Careta's daughter."

Balboa swung around violently. "The princess? What's the matter? What happened?"

"She managed somehow to slip away," said Rodrigo. "Garavito has gone into the woods in pursuit of her."

"Which way?"

Colmenares pointed. "But where are you going — ?"

"After her! After Garavito!" Balboa flung back as he ran. "Take charge until I return, Colmenares. You and Hurtado."

He passed Hurtado with a group of bound captives.

"Where are you going?" demanded his lieutenant.

"After the cacique's daughter. She escaped."

"I know, but Garavito has gone — "

"All the more reason for me to go!" shouted Balboa.

"But the natives! Those who escaped are no doubt lurking there. It's dangerous." But Balboa was already disappearing into the jungle.

He fought through the tangled undergrowth, slashing at the sinuous vines with his sword. Now and again he stopped to listen, then struggled on. The jungle was black and eerie.

Even the brilliant stars overhead had a mocking glitter to his frantic eyes. How would he ever find her? What strange madness had sent him on this search?

He stopped again, breathless.

At that moment a few yards to the right, he heard a man's voice raised in triumph. A desperate thrashing in the branches. Then a high scream stabbed the air and was abruptly silenced.

How he reached them he could not, afterward, remember clearly. He only knew that later he bled from a hundred body scratches.

"Let her go, Andrés!"

Both heads jerked back. Luaia gasped, then cried out in pain as Garavito's fingers tightened cruelly on her arm.

"I will not!" Garavito's voice was harsh. "She's my slave."

"Not so, Andrés!" Balboa's big fist caught him squarely on the jaw.

Garavito fell back limply into a thicket. The girl, freed, turned once more to flee.

"Wait!" Balboa's voice was persuasive.

Luaia hesitated, her body trembling from exhaustion. Slowly, as a man approaches a wild thing, fearful of alarming it into flight, Balboa drew near.

He touched her shivering shoulder compassionately.

"Do not be afraid, Luaia. I promise that you shall come to no harm," he said in halting native tongue.

Her eyes, looking up at him, filled suddenly with tears.

"Ai — ee!" She slid to a hopeless mourning heap at his feet.

When Andrés Garavito had recovered consciousness, he stumbled sullenly ahead of Balboa, who was half carrying the princess.

Bartolomé Hurtado came to meet them.

"We have found the cacique's hoard of provisions, just as

Garavito and Juan Alonzo said. There is plenty of food and gold and —"

"Very well," said Balboa, weariness filling mind and body, "divide it into loads for carrying. We'll take it back to the brigantines."

The captives were made to march ahead of the soldiers, carrying the spoils. They were not mistreated, however, and the cacique and his family were made to carry no burdens.

"You treat these people like Christians," said Andrés Garavito scornfully. "They are infidels, Vasco Núñez, and can understand only force."

"I am not convinced of that," replied Balboa.

"Ah, well," Garavito shrugged, "you are, of course, the leader of this expedition. It is not for me to criticize, eh? I was only a means to an end, I see. I may not even expect favors for my part in this raid."

"But indeed you may," said Balboa. "At Darien, the spoils are divided into equal shares."

"And the slaves?"

"They, too," replied Balboa hesitantly. He knew the desire for the princess still burned in Garavito's heart. Occasionally, the soldier would walk ahead with the slaves on the pretense of keeping them in line, although that was not the task assigned to him. Luaia, marching between her father and her eldest brother, stared through him with a royal haughtiness that Balboa secretly applauded. Despite the miserable turn of affairs, she was still a princess of Coyba, proud though in slavery. Her father, too, and her brothers stepped stoically along, seeming to ignore their unhappy circumstance.

The Indians were plainly awed by the brigantines, however. Even the cacique's eyes grew wide with marveling. Never had they beheld such great ships. They regarded them and the strangers from distant lands who had, it was said, built these floating mansions, with less hate now than respect. Surely, these must be powerful beings — and no doubt favored by all the gods of heaven and earth.

Balboa escorted the cacique about the ship as if he were a visiting dignitary. He took personal charge of Luaia, to see that no one harmed or insulted her.

As the ship entered the Darien harbor, Garavito approached him.

"I have decided to relinquish my share of the spoil — "

"What!" Balboa stared at him in astonishment. "Why?"

"And to accept only one slave for my share of this expedition."

"But — but you are entitled to more." His blue eyes searched Garavito's dark ones. "Why?"

"That I may have my choice of all the slaves," said Andrés Garavito slyly. "Surely that is not too much to ask for my part in your success." He moistened his lips. "It was my plan, remember."

"What slave do you want?" asked Balboa, though he well knew the answer.

"The Princess Luaia," came the inexorable words.

Even though expected, the bold request sent fury scorching through Balboa.

"No!" he roared.

"But why not?" Andrés Garavito's eyes flashed rebellion. "It is a simple enough request — one slave among so many."

"No!" roared Balboa again. "I say no. Any other — not the cacique's daughter. I have seen the dislike of you in her eyes. I have seen the distaste — "

"I can put humility there instead. I will teach the little infidel not to scorn a white man's favor."

Balboa's eyes were brilliant. Hand on his halberd, he leaned toward Garavito. "Remember that I am the commander here, Andrés Garavito. Do not presume upon our former acquaintance. Do not try my patience. The matter is settled."

Andrés Garavito's face darkened with impotent anger. Without a word, he turned and walked off down the deck.

It took some minutes for the rage to leave Balboa. He felt weak from the surprising force of it. He looked after his old friend of whom he had made an enemy. But he promised himself that he would make it up to Andrés. He would give him more than his rightful share of the spoils. He would win him back in time.

Yet he was not sorry for his decision. The cacique's lovely daughter should not become the slave of a man she scorned. He had promised no harm should come to her.

The people at Darien were elated at the return of the brigantines with both supplies and slaves.

Francisco Pizarro, whom Balboa had left in charge, suggested an immediate division of the natives among the colonists.

All gathered together in the plaza.

"Never have I seen such fine slaves," said Fernando Múñoz to Balboa. "And never more beautiful maidens than these of Coyba. I swear I would as soon wed one of them as any Spanish girl."

"And the cacique's daughter — she is the most lovely of all," said Francisco Pizarro. "I hear one of the Spaniards who dwelt with Careta is eager to possess her."

Balboa nodded curtly, his eyes on the cacique and his family who were being led into the square, their chains clanking a pitiful dirge as they walked. Luaia's eyes were downcast and her lips tremulous, but she walked steadily and as gracefully as she could with the metal on her slender bare ankles.

Suddenly her father, the cacique Careta fell to his knees, his eyes searching out Balboa.

"For what reason do you treat me with such cruelty?" he asked beseechingly. "I received you with kindness, yet you returned my hospitality with this! Behold these chains. Look on the misery of those who but lately received you as an honored guest. Set us free, I pray, and we will serve you not as unwilling slaves but as willing friends. Riches you desire and food. Both shall be yours, if you be merciful." He stretched out his arms to Balboa earnestly. "Do you doubt me? Then take my only daughter to be your wife — she shall be a pledge of friendship."

At these words, Balboa was filled with remorse at what he had done. Truly, he had greatly wronged this people. He had sought to excuse himself from guilt because of the need of the Darien colony. But now he saw that his only justification must be the righting of the wrong.

His eyes rested gently on the face of the Princess Luaia. He was struck anew with her noble beauty. He stepped toward her, looking deep into her soft eyes.

"Luaia," he said, "are you willing?"

Her lashes fell. "I am, master." There was no fear nor distaste in her manner, only the proper shyness of a maid offered in wedlock.

Balboa took a deep breath. "I accept your offer of friendship," he told Careta.

The entire gathering, Spaniards and natives alike, shouted excitedly. For the most part, all were pleased. Here and there, however, was a dissatisfied man, suspicious of the cacique's word, or disappointed in not receiving any Indian slaves.

Francisco Pizarro ventured to remonstrate. "Are you certain that this is wise? These infidels are rarely to be trusted."

"I have given my word," said Balboa staunchly. "The friendship of this cacique will be of value to us, I am convinced. We are in need of native allies in our struggle with the wilderness."

"Aye, he is right," agreed Colmenares, stepping forward. "Careta's knowledge of the land and the source of its riches will be of great aid to us."

Thus the pact between the cacique Careta and Vasco Núñez de Balboa was completed. The Indians of Coyba were released and remained three days at Darien where they were entertained generously. Many were the wonders that these simple people saw. Many were the presents they received.

Careta was astonished at the Spanish musicians playing their trumpets, flutes, guitars and viols so harmoniously. He gazed, openmouthed, at the war horses and the strong armor.

Vasco Núñez de Balboa and the Princess Luaia were married with solemn Indian rites on the third day, and Balboa was never to feel their union less binding because unhallowed by the Church.

After promising Careta that the Spaniards would aid him against his neighboring enemy Ponca, Balboa allowed them to return to Coyba. When they were nearly out of sight, he turned to Luaia, who was looking after her people wistfully.

"I have no wish to keep you with me against your will," he said tenderly. "Say the word, and you shall return to your father's house."

Luaia, however, merely turned her face up to him. Gratitude glowed like starlight in her eyes.

"I will remain," she said.

"Then," said Balboa, "you forgive me for what I did to your people? You do not dislike me?" He waited for her answer as eagerly as a boy.

"Our people are taught to worship the sun," said Luaia

slowly. "We are taught to adore the sky." She dropped her eyes shyly. "Your hair is like the sun and your eyes like the sky. There is warmth in your smile and vision of great deeds in your glance. Therefore, master, to me you are like the sun and the sky."

CHAPTER XIX

AN ASTOUNDING REVELATION

THE CAMPAIGN AGAINST PONCA, ENEMY OF CARETA, WAS SUCCESS-
ful. Hearing of the Spanish invasion of his realms, Ponca and
his people fled, leaving the field to the Spaniards and their allies
of Coyba.

Having obtained a large store of provisions and some gold
in the deserted village, Balboa was well-disposed to visit a
neighboring but more friendly cacique. Before leaving Darien,
he had received a native envoy from the province of Comogra.
A councilor of Careta, having disagreed with his superior, left
Coyba and joined a tribe ruled by the cacique Comogre. Here
this man, Jura by name, became a high officer under his new
lord.

Jura had been much impressed by the prowess of the Spaniards, and convinced his chief that it would be better to have
the friendship than the enmity of these men.

Therefore, Balboa received an invitation to visit the country
of this prudent Indian.

He questioned Careta about the province of Comogra.

"It is a land of great wealth," replied the cacique. "Food and
gold, they say, are both plentiful there. Moreover, Comogre
has an army of three thousand powerful warriors."

Marching north with his men, Balboa came to a broad plain,
fertile and beautiful, which stretched twelve leagues to the foot
of a great mountain.

"Truly," said Balboa to Colmenares, "this province of Comogra is well favored."

The cacique himself came forth to greet the Spaniards. With him were his seven handsome sons and his officer, Jura.

The cacique's village was near the river Comogra which, rising in the mountains beyond, watered the wide plateau and then flowed on south through a rugged country.

The Spaniards were welcomed with ceremony and escorted to the town. The most prominent structure was, of course, the dwelling of the cacique. Its spacious elegance amazed the Europeans. One hundred and fifty paces long and eighty wide, it was built of great wooden beams and further reinforced by walls of stone. Entering, Balboa saw that the ceilings were of intricately carved wood, while the floors were decorated with unusual artistry.

"Never have I seen in Terra Firma such a native building," said Balboa.

Pleased, the cacique led them into all the rooms. He showed them his large storehouse of grains and vegetables, the underground room where his meats were preserved — venison, fowl and wild boar. An adjoining cellar was stocked with earthen vessels and wooden casks filled with native wines made of roots and grain.

Last of all, Comogre led his guests into the sacred inner room. Here the mummies of his ancestors hung from cotton ropes tied to the ceiling. Masks of gold were over their faces. The room was crowded with these eerie forms of the departed and the cacique insisted on leading the Spaniards to each in turn, bowing in reverence as he solemnly introduced the dead to the living.

Balboa shivered as they came out.

"Quite a lively gathering, eh, Colmenares?"

An expressive grunt was his companion's only reply.

Comogre and his sons now escorted their Spanish guests to comfortable dwelling places, where each man was given the services of slaves for the duration of the visit. Food and drink were set before them. Entertainments were given by Indian dancers. Nothing was spared that might make the colonists' stay more pleasant.

As a final magnificent gesture, the son of Comogre presented to the Spaniards gold worth about four thousand pesos and wrought into beautiful likenesses of men, animals and birds. With greedy delight, the Spaniards immediately brought out scales and melting instruments and began to weigh and divide the gold, first taking out the king's royal fifth.

Balboa remonstrated, begging them to desist.

"Moreover," he said, "by melting the gold you will destroy the beauty of the pieces wrought so artistically by our Indian hosts."

But the fever was upon his men. "Would you expect us to carry these gold figures all the way back to Darien, when we can melt them here and make the burden easier?"

Balboa shrugged, seeing that they were determined. But, looking about at the assembled natives, he saw puzzlement on every face, then dawning resentment. The cacique, Comogre, however, said nothing.

Presently the soldiers were quarreling, then fists and hot words flew. Each accused the other of taking more than his share. In vain, Balboa tried to pacify them.

Scorn flared in the dark eyes of the eldest son of Comogre. Suddenly he thrust his way through the shouting men. His fist crashed down upon the scales, scattering the gold.

"What strange dispute is this, Christians? Why do you shout at one another? Why do you quarrel over this trifling treasure?"

Amazed at his act and the ringing disdain in his voice, the Spaniards stood still, staring at him.

The brave youth continued. "Is it for this yellow product of the earth that you leave your far homes to suffer hardships and perils in alien country? Is it for this that you invade the lands of those who have done you no harm, bringing calamity where before was peace? If this is the strange hunger that torments such powerful warriors, hear me now. I know of a region where gold is more abundant than your dreams of it."

Most of the Spaniards were speechless, but Francisco Pizarro spoke boldly:

"Tell us then, son of Comogre. Where is this land of fabled treasure?"

The youth raised an arm, pointing southward. "It lies there, beyond those mountains and over the sea."

"A sea!" exclaimed Balboa. "You say that southward lies a sea? How large?"

"Very vast," replied Comogre's son. "The people there navigate by means of sails and oars such as yours, though their vessels are not so large. You, too, must sail across the water to reach this land of gold."

"A southern sea," murmured Balboa, his eyes rapt upon the young cacique. He grew breathless with the thought of it. To be the first Spaniard to look upon this great new water — ah, that would indeed be an achievement! Could it be said then that his rule in Darien was barren of accomplishment? Could it be said that he, Vasco Núñez de Balboa, was an upstart debtor forcing the command from those better suited to it? Would not his name spread then through all of Spain — yes, even to the village of Xeres de los Caballeros where his father and his brother Gonzalo would hear of it with pride at last?

Eagerly, he listened to the next words of the Indian prince.

"But the journey to the sea is perilous. There are many sierras and treacherous rivers to cross. Many fierce tribes will dispute your passage. Some are cannibals who are called Caribs, lawless and wandering. There is, too, a powerful chieftain called Tumanama who dwells in a province richer in gold than any other in these mountains. He will resist your invasion with all his strength."

Balboa listened to this tale of the difficulties which confronted him, but was unimpressed. Struggles? Dangers? He had become used to them, and for what cause? A little grain, some bread and meat to sustain a bare physical existence; gold to assuage a greed which, like some pagan dragon, grew more demanding and stretched great jaws for additional tribute. True, like all his men, he had deemed these sufficient aims of wilderness life.

But now, for the first time, he envisioned a goal that pulled at the very center of his being, awakening old dreams, fashioning new, filling his soul with the same thunderous urgency that had first brought him to these lands. He felt as if some part of him, slumbering for more than a decade, had come vigorously awake.

"But how do we know that his words are true?" asked some of the men.

"Aye, what proof has the son of Comogre?" asked Fernando Múñoz, pushing forward.

"Slaves whom we have taken in battle have told of this great water and the rich land which surrounds it," replied the son of Comogre earnestly. He lifted an arm. "Xanala, come here!"

"I come, master." The old Indian stepped forward stiffly. The passage of many years had rutted his skin, but his eyes were bright with a lifetime's wisdom.

"In his youth Xanala, one of our own people, was a captive

of the cacique beyond the mountains. He can tell you that I speak the truth."

Slowly and with a candor that could not be doubted, Xanala verified his young lord's statements.

"Nevertheless, if you are still unconvinced," said the son of Comogre, "I myself will accompany you as guide. If my story is false, then take my life as forfeit."

"Your honesty is evident, son of Comogre," answered Balboa. "Accept our thanks for this valuable information. But — " his eyes searched those of the young native, "for what reason did you give it to us?"

The Indian's gaze was steady. "That you may aid us against our enemies through whose lands you must pass. You covet gold. We desire power and deliverance from hostile neighbors, so that we may live fearless and at peace. Just as we have many slaves, so many of our people have been taken captive. Whether conquerors or conquered, we are continually harassed on every side. With your armies combined with ours, such a great victory should result that we may live untroubled for a long time."

The Spaniards remained a few days more with Comogre before returning to Darien. The natives, puzzled but anxious to please their guests, were baptized into the Christian religion.

To the son of Comogre was given the name of Carlos. Gifts were exchanged and the Spaniards were presented with seventy slaves.

Balboa set out for Darien with but one eager thought in mind. He must recruit the thousand men which the son of Comogre, now called Carlos, had said were necessary for the journey. He must prepare for the great expedition to the southern sea.

CHAPTER XX

THE HURRICANE

Two days after his return to Darien, Balboa rode out to the fields to see how the new slaves were getting along with the cultivation of the crops. The heat was oppressive. Abnormally so, it seemed to Balboa. Clouds darkened the sky, but the sun's rays came through dimly with a queer glare harder for the eye to bear than direct light.

He passed among the natives, speaking kindly, offering advice to some, showing novices how to hold the implements and work the ground. He was pleased with the thriving maize, feeling again his first delight at the rapid luxuriant growth of everything in this climate. Crops grew and were harvested twice as quickly as in Spain. Cabbages, beets, lettuces and other seeds from Europe flourished and were ready for picking in ten days; cucumbers, in less than twenty days; pumpkins and melons were ripe twenty-eight days after the seeds were pushed into the fertile earth.

It was upon the great fields of maize, however, that the Spaniards depended for sustenance. This maize, or hobba, as it was often called in Darien, was used to make bread. Small garden strips were also devoted to the raising of that delicious native root, the potato. Indians were digging them now, crouching over the hills, bare backs streaming with perspiration.

When Balboa rode up on his huge war horse, they greeted him with awe.

"Here, bring me one," said Balboa, and dismounted.

One of the natives hastened forward, his two joined hands heaped with the earth-stained vegetables.

"Not ten," Balboa laughed, "only one." He took a potato and rubbed it on his doublet to remove the soil. Then he bit into it, his strong teeth crunching through the white starchy meat.

"Mm. Good." His eyes fell on the natives watching him. He took the rest of the potatoes from the slave's hands and flung them to the workers. "Here. Eat some yourselves while you rest a bit from the labor. Saints of heaven, how hot it is!"

"The wind gods come," said one of the natives ominously. His eyes rolled upward. His lips moved soundlessly in some ancient pagan prayer.

A murmur of fearful assent ran among the other slaves.

"A storm, you mean?" Balboa spoke sharply. "Soon?"

The natives nodded.

"But not a breath of wind stirs. See, how still and drooping all the leaves are. Nothing moves," Balboa protested.

"Not here." The Indian turned back stoically to his digging. "But over there the wind gods gather forces. Soon ride this way, destruction in their giant fists."

"Perhaps it will not strike here," suggested Balboa optimistically.

"Perhaps," the natives agreed, but without hope.

Even as he turned away, Balboa could feel the change in the air. No longer was it heavy and motionless. It was stirring, not quickly but as if it were a great sheet of glass being slowly pushed back.

Across the fields from the town's edge, a woman's voice called anxiously. He saw that Luaia was running toward him, stumbling in her haste, her dark hair floating behind her.

Balboa swung to the saddle, shouting to the Spanish overseers as he galloped by them.

"Get everyone to cover! Take what crops you can carry off in time!"

He pulled sharply on the reins. Luaia flung herself at his leg braced in the stirrup, gripping it with both her strong slender hands.

Her head tipped back, eyes black with fear.

"Vas-co! The wind gods — they are angry!"

"So I've been told," said Balboa soothingly. He reached down and put his great hands around her little waist, drawing her up into the saddle before him.

"Ai-ee!" She clutched him desperately. "I was afraid. I came for you."

He put his chin down, moving it comfortingly against her smooth silken head.

"Do not be afraid, Luaia. I will keep you safe."

He touched the spurs to his horse, sent it galloping into Darien. The wind was coming now, driving, whirling. The colonists ran for shelter, shouting, calling to one another. By the time Balboa reached his own cabin with Luaia, broken branches, small bushes were sailing through the streets and the air was a weird yellow-green.

Inside their cabin, Balboa slammed the door and bolted fast the windows. He could feel the wind driving at the thick log walls, shrieking at the crevices. Luaia lit a candle and put it on the rough table where it flickered from the small gusts through the cracks like a frightened bird.

Balboa stood in the half-dark. The dimness and the tumult all around him entered his heart. His thoughts were like the sickening color of the outside world — yellow-green, the color of despair. This hurricane would flatten all the maize, destroy all the painstaking labor of the planting. This rain that poured from the heavens like a great ocean would flood the fields. Nothing would be left. Flattened, torn, blown, watersoaked . . . everything.

His hands clenched together painfully. His teeth bearing down against his lip brought blood to it, and he tasted it, uncaring. In an instant, without warning, because of what natives spoke of as the wind gods, the labor of months became naught. Wind gods! Wind devils, more like!

He laughed — another harsh sound in a world full of hideous uproar. The cabin rocked in the gale. Maybe the cabin would be blown away or pummeled to a crazy heap of sticks.

Luaia came over to him, walking in her soft light way. The fear that had been in her face a while ago in the fields had gone. She appeared unaware of the roaring, blasting thunder and the fierce swift glare of lightning that was nearly continuous.

He felt her hand touching his set cheek. His rage broke, crumbling away before that understanding caress. Tears came to his eyes. He shook his head to clear his vision of them. Weep before his wife, show her the weakness of him? He must not!

"Vas-co."

He smiled at her, closing her in his arms. He liked to hear her speak his name, as if it were two instead of one.

"Yes, Luaia?"

"I wish to explain," she said softly in the careful Spanish she had learned. "I was afraid, not for myself, but — for you." She rushed on. "Without you, I should not wish to remain here. I should go immediately to join my ancestors."

He saw the earnest intensity of her face.

"I, too," he said wonderingly. "I feel the same, Luaia."

When the hurricane was finally over, he went with the other colonists to the fields. It was even worse than he had expected. The entire harvest was either swept away by the winds or completely buried bv rubbish washed down by waters from the mountains.

With bleak faces, they began to repair the damage. Repair the damage! Pitifully little could be restored. Here and there, under the piled up debris, a few vegetables, some bruised fruit. That was all.

The wraith that had been hovering over the little colony for so long was now in their midst. Balboa could feel it stalking by his side as he toiled with the native slaves, doggedly clearing the gardens. He could see it peering at him from the eyes of fellow Spaniards. He could hear it speak from Indian lips. Most loudly of all, he could hear it in Luaia's patient, uncomplaining silence. Starvation! A merciless specter with an appetite for pioneers.

As if the ruin of the crops were not sufficient misfortune, some of the more adventurous slaves had escaped in the confusion, preferring the hurricane and possible freedom to remaining at Darien.

The second day after the storm Balboa set out for the woods with Leonçico, hoping to find some wild game. The trees were broken and twisted. The jungle, a tangle of wreckage. Even the bright parrots, usually so noisily numerous, were scarce.

Suddenly, Leonçico bristled. Halting, Balboa heard it too — a faint whimpering a few yards away. He looked, but could see nothing except a wind-tossed heap of lumber and broken vines.

Leonçico bounded forward, however, sniffing at the pile. He began to whine, to scratch at the branches.

Balboa followed. He listened, bidding Leonçico to be silent. The whimpering had ceased. The hound circled then, smelling among the leaves. He yelped once and began to pull at something. A strip of yellow cloth. Simultaneously, the whimpering started again, growing louder with terror. Unmistakably a woman.

Balboa's arms strained at the branches imprisoning her. He pulled, pushed, spoke now and again in reassurance. The Indian maid lay huddled, one leg pinioned under a thick, cruelly heavy tree limb. When finally, grunting with exertion, he lifted it, she tried to rise, but the limp leg would not hold her. She fell back with a cry of pain.

"It is broken," said Balboa compassionately.

He recognized the little maid as one of Hurtado's slaves. She was of the tribe of Cemaco, original lord of Darien. No doubt she had tried to flee into the woods, hoping to regain her freedom. But the hurricane had felled a tree to stop her flight. He had a brief vision of the girl running through a night of howling terror, then caught like a trapped animal while the winds piled debris over her as earth is thrown over a grave.

He lifted her gently, saw her face pale with the pain of moving. Yet no cry came now from her clenched lips.

"What is your name, little maid?"

Her eyes stared up at him, agony in their depths.

"Fulvia," she said obediently, but it was more like a moan.

"You were fleeing?"

No answer, except a frightened movement of her body.

"I am taking you back to Darien, Fulvia."

She was limply resigned.

"But no harm will come to you," he said soothingly.

Back in Darien, he carried the maid to Bartolomé Hurtado's cabin.

Hurtado came forward. Seeing the girl, he cried out angrily.

"Fulvia! Where did you find her?" He reached out and jerked her from Balboa's arms. "The little vixen escaped in the hurricane."

"Careful. She's hurt. Her leg —"

Hurtado's face was knotted with fury. "I'll teach her to try to escape. She's one of seven who ran away. Where are the others? Where are they?" He seized her hair, twisting it so that her eyes rolled, staring.

"I know not. Truly, master, I know not!"

"Stop, Hurtado!" Balboa's voice was grim. "She's hurt, I tell you. Her leg is broken."

"I care not! She deserves to be punished —"

"She's been punished enough. She's lain alone in the forest for almost two days, pinned under a tree, her leg broken and no one to hear her cries for help."

"A crippled slave — the only one of the seven to be returned to me!" He let her fall. The little maid screamed in pain.

Balboa stooped and caught her up.

"None of the seven has been returned," he said sternly. "This slave is mine, Bartolomé Hurtado. I will buy her from you."

"But I —"

"I said I will buy her from you, Bartolomé. She is a cripple, but I will pay you full price for her."

"Very well," said Hurtado, his face sulky. "She's of no value to me now."

Depression swept over Balboa as he carried the native girl back to his dwelling. Bartolomé Hurtado had changed. The hard life in Terra Firma, the threat of starvation, the greed for gold had made him a different man from the soldier whom he had rescued in the shipwreck, and had lived neighbor to at

Salvatierre. He was hard now, hard as the craggy mountains towering over this swampy, wind-ripped valley.

In his own doorway, he called for Luaia. She came forward at once.

"Fulvia," she said in surprise. "What has happened?"

"Her leg is broken. I brought her from Hurtado's. I—I have purchased her to be your servant, Luaia."

"She is hurt." Luaia's eyes were soft with pity. "Lay her on the mat in the corner, Vas-co. I will tend her."

He put the maid down, then turned to leave. Luaia followed him to the door.

"You have such kindness," she said softly. "I know why you have bought her. That Hurtado, it is said he does not treat his slaves well."

"Nonsense," blustered Balboa. "One can buy a cripple cheaper. When her leg mends, she will make you a good servant, Luaia—and you will see I have made a good bargain."

He went out, avoiding the smiling disbelief in her eyes. He must pay Hurtado. He must find Juan Gúñoz, who was skillful at binding broken limbs.

He became aware of excitement in the settlement. Rodrigo de Colmenares shouted at him as he ran in the direction of the harbor.

"Sails have been sighted, Vasco Núñez! It is thought to be the ship of Juan de Valdivia, returned from Española!"

Balboa breathed a prayer of thanksgiving. Juan de Valdivia at last. Supplies and perhaps reinforcements from Santo Domingo!

CHAPTER XXI

THE QUEST FOR THE GOLDEN TEMPLE OF DAVAIVE

VALDIVIA'S CARAVEL BROUGHT PROVISIONS, AS BALBOA HAD HOPED, but only sufficient for a few days.

"His Excellency, the governor, sent a commission appointing you his lieutenant in Urabá," said Juan de Valdivia, embracing Balboa affectionately. "Moreover, the royal treasurer, Miguel de Pasamonte, has promised to speak in your behalf to his friends in the Spanish court."

This was good news indeed. The commission was particularly welcome, and Balboa knew he needed influence with King Ferdinand.

"Diego Columbus has also promised to send us more provisions as soon as ships which they expect momentarily from Spain arrive."

Balboa's heart lightened. The future looked more favorable. He clapped his good friend Valdivia on the shoulder, then looked past him at the crowd gathered around another boatful rowed ashore from the caravel.

His eyes questioned. "Someone in particular has come with you from Santo Domingo?"

Valdivia smiled broadly. "Very particular. They are greeting Juan de Caicedo's wife."

"His wife — here!"

"Aye. She insisted on coming, although we told her she

would be the only white woman in the settlement. She seemed only the more determined."

"Brave woman," said Balboa and strode toward the growing group around the arrival.

As he walked, he wondered if the sight of a Spanish woman would affect in any way his devotion to Luaia. Would he find her more lovely than his own native mate?

Juan de Caicedo, almost inarticulate with pleasure, introduced him.

"I am pleased to meet so courageous and devoted a woman," said Balboa gallantly, and bent over her hand. Straightening, he looked at her with interest.

She was dark, with fair enough features and a friendly smile that showed white even teeth. But in no way did her loveliness approach Luaia's, and Vasco Núñez de Balboa returned to his own cabin, satisfied. The appearance of Juan de Caicedo's wife had settled once and for all the question that sometimes bothered him. Aye, Luaia's beauty was more than a match for that of any Spanish woman. Never would he regret his choice.

Within a week, Juan de Valdivia was sent back to Santo Domingo with a request for immediate aid for the starving colonists. He carried with him the king's fifth for the royal treasurer, Pasamonte.

The colonists also entrusted to Valdivia sums to pay off debts which they had left in Santo Domingo, Balboa himself sending enough to his creditors to clear his obligations completely. Balboa also gave Juan de Valdivia additional gold to be transported from Santo Domingo to his father and brother in Spain.

"It is the first I have been able to send to my family since I arrived in Española years ago with Bastidas," he said happily. "I hope they have not despaired of me." He put a letter into Valdivia's hand. "Give this to Diego Columbus. Tell him what we have learned concerning the great southern sea and the wealth of the surrounding country. We need a thousand men for the expedition, according to Comogre's son, Carlos. Ask him to use his influence in this important matter."

"I will do my best," said Juan de Valdivia, clasping his hand. "I can see in your eyes, Vasco Núñez, how much it means to you. You have changed," he went on thoughtfully. "You are somehow quieter and less restless."

"I have a purpose now," said Balboa, "which I had not before."

His eyes went to the ship, and grew anxious. Valdivia smiled. "Aye, it does not look any too seaworthy, does it?" He shrugged. "Ah, well, it brought me here. It will get me safely back to Santo Domingo, I think."

Suddenly, watching his friend's face, a coldness came over Balboa — a premonition of disaster.

"I do not think I should let you go!" he exclaimed. "I have a fear I shall never behold your loyal face again in this world."

Valdivia laughed heartily. "You have become superstitious, Vasco Núñez. There, too, you have changed. You speak like a woman with visions."

"Nevertheless — "

"Nevertheless, my caravel sails in less than half an hour," said Valdivia. "Farewell, my good friend. I shall return in a few weeks and with me a thousand soldiers for your expedition to the sea."

He took his place in the waiting boat and was rowed out to the caravel. Climbing the ladder, he turned and waved once to Balboa.

As the ship sailed out of sight, Balboa bent and patted Leonçico's head. He could not shake off the feeling of foreboding. He felt unaccountably lonely.

Striding through the settlement, he was aware of eyes upon him, questioning, worrying, demanding eyes. "What is to be done now, Vasco Núñez de Balboa?" Over and over again, that query. Unspoken except in a look, a searching glance as he passed. Yet making a louder impression on his mind than words. "What is to be done now, Vasco Núñez de Balboa? You are our leader. We are feeling the pinch of hunger. What is to be done now?"

What was to be done? He shrugged. Barring the unlikely miracle of manna raining from heaven, there was only one thing to be done. They must undertake foraging expeditions into the surrounding country.

There had been rumors from time to time, Balboa remembered, concerning a reputedly wealthy region called Davaive.

He decided to question Luaia about it, for he had heard many times from the natives of various tribes of a certain golden temple of Davaive.

He threw open the door of his dwelling and said abruptly: "What do you know of the golden temple of Davaive, Luaia?"

Her hands dropped from the mat of grasses she was weaving. She came forward obediently, but with disturbed eyes.

"Vas-co, you are leaving again?"

"Aye. We need food." He did not meet her eyes, but repeated his question.

"Davaive?" She spoke thoughtfully, as if trying dutifully to recall every detail and rumor concerning the province. "Davaive was an Indian princess, so they say, who possessed divine powers and was very wise and good — "

"Yes, yes, but that's not important — "

Her eyes rebuked his impatience. "But it is, Vas-co, for after her death this temple you speak of was built in which to worship her — just as," she explained carefully, "you build temples to pray to your great goddess, the Holy Mary."

"It's not the same thing at all," protested Balboa irritably. He had labored long and earnestly only the night before to explain to Luaia the mysteries of the one true religion, and now she confounded him with something like this! Comparing the Blessed Virgin to a pagan princess!

"I have displeased you!" wailed Luaia. "Ai-ee, forgive me, dear Vas-co. I have said wrong."

"Never mind," said Balboa soothingly. "Just tell me about this temple."

"Every year," said Luaia, pushing the words from her lips cautiously, "it is said that the natives and caciques of certain countries send golden tributes and great treasure there. It is said to contain great wealth." She moved her shoulders doubtfully. "But I do not know. I have never talked with anyone who has seen this temple."

Two days later, Balboa sailed with one hundred and seventy picked men in two brigantines and a number of native canoes. Nine leagues east, he reached the mouth of a river ten times wider than the Darien.

Rodrigo de Colmenares took one-third of the men to explore the stream, making his way toward the mountains along the eastern coast. Balboa and his men followed a branching tributary which flowed southward. After thirty miles they reached the native village of the cacique named Davaive.

It was completely deserted! Balboa suspected that the cacique Cemaco, tireless in seeking revenge against the Spaniards for having driven him from his lands, had warned Davaive.

Alas for the hopes of the soldiers of finding the golden tem-

ple! No Indians appeared from whom they might extort information about it, and certainly there was no trace of it. The
country was swampy, unsuitable for agriculture or even fruit
trees. Disappointed at not finding any provisions, the Spaniards nevertheless were faintly cheered by discovering in the
houses jewels and gold amounting in worth to seven thousand
castellanos. They seized, as well, a hundred bows and arrows
and native furniture.

"Ugh, I like not the look of this country. 'Twould be foolhardy to attempt exploration of these morasses without guides,"
said Balboa.

"Ah, well," said Bartolomé Hurtado, fingering a wrought
gold bracelet he had found, "our trip was not entirely in vain,
since, at least, we found some treasure."

"But we can't eat it!" barked Balboa. It annoyed him to see
how tenderly Hurtado touched the inanimate metal. For contrast, his recent treatment of the little Fulvia kept recurring in
his mind. Greed, he thought reluctantly, was warping Hurtado's very features. His eyes had been frank and full of laughter; now they were narrow and calculating. His voice had been
clear and boyish; it was hard now — except when gold was
mentioned, when it grew husky with a sort of passionate under-
tone. Balboa could no longer be sure that what Hurtado said
and what he thought were the same.

All the booty was put into two canoes taken from the Indian
settlement and Balboa's company returned to the gulf of Urabá.
Here a great tempest almost wrecked the ships and the booty
was lost in the sea.

Managing to rejoin Colmenares, they made their way up a
stream which they named, because of its dark waters, Rio
Negro. Ascending a branch of this river, they reached a prov-

ince ruled by a cacique named Abibaiba. His people lived in houses built in great trees. These dwellings were made to resist the strongest winds.

The Spaniards were amazed at these houses and greatly wondered at the giant trees. Eight men, joining fingertips, could barely embrace some of them.

The natives had drawn their reed ladders up after them into their lofty homes and would not come down, despite peaceable entreaties and, later, outright threats. Only when the soldiers took axes and began to chop at the trunks, did the chief, Abibaiba, and his two sons reluctantly descend.

But he had no gold, said Abibaiba, for he had never considered it much good. However, if that was what the Spaniards desired, he would be glad to get some for them in the surrounding mountains. He promised to return, leaving his wife and sons as hostages.

They waited in vain for Abibaiba. It was evident after the day set for his reappearance had passed, that this cacique had no intention of returning.

"Not exactly family men," said Colmenares, indicating the chief's subdued wife and children, "these caciques of Terra Firma."

The Spaniards, after various other excursions into neighboring Indian countries, returned to Darien with the provisions and slaves they had taken.

"At least, we will eat," thought Balboa, and was glad that for a while at least starvation would not add to the hazards of life in Darien.

Also, he felt that a beginning had been made in subduing and colonizing the rest of Urabá, for Bartolomé Hurtado had been left with thirty men in a native village on the Rio Negro.

He was to hold the province until further settlement was possible.

Not many weeks after Balboa's return with the expedition, however, a native barque arrived at the settlement. It held Hurtado and only twelve men.

The colonists crowded around them excitedly.

"Where are the others?" demanded Balboa.

"Alas!" Hurtado spread his hands expressively.

"They have — perished?"

"Aye. We alone survive." He shivered. "Rio Negro! 'Tis well named. Black waters — black misfortune."

CHAPTER XXII

THE PLOT AGAINST THE SETTLEMENT

BRIEFLY, BARTOLOMÉ HURTADO TOLD HIS STORY OF DISASTER. Illness, he said, had overcome two thirds of his men, already weakened by exposure and hardship. Therefore he had sent them back to Darien along with twenty-four slaves that had been captured.

The great canoe which bore them down the Rio Negro was heavily loaded. They had gone only a short way when attacked by Cemaco and his warriors in four canoes. Able to make but weak resistance, all except two were either slain or drowned when they jumped into the river. The two survivors managed to escape by concealing themselves beneath spreading branches of trees floating on the water. They made their way back to Hurtado who, alarmed and discouraged, decided to return with the remnant of his force to Darien.

Moreover, he told the colonists that he had heard rumors that natives throughout the countryside were massing for an attack on the settlement.

"This same Cemaco seeks revenge because we have taken his land," said Hurtado somberly.

"But only lately he sent us thirty slaves to work in the fields," protested Balboa. "Certainly that does not indicate ill will."

"I only tell you what I have heard," said Hurtado a trifle testily. "Believe it or not, as you will."

Some of the colonists received the news with alarm. Some were incredulous, some indifferent. As the days went by and nothing untoward occurred, most of them forgot it entirely. Balboa himself inclined to the opinion that Hurtado had snatched at the story as an excuse to return to the comparative comfort and security of Darien.

One day, however, as he was about to ride into the fields as was his habit, the little maid Fulvia approached him, her eyes red from weeping.

"Master! Oh, master!"

"Aye," he said gently, "what would you, Fulvia?"

Instead of answering she burst into such a wailing and rush of tears that Balboa stood back, amazed. It seemed an incredible amount of grief from so small a maid.

He shifted his great frame from one foot to the other, waiting for the force of her sorrow to abate. Then, when it did not, he touched her awkwardly.

"Tell me what troubles you. Is it your leg which pains you again?"

"Ai-ee!" came the far from satisfactory reply. "Ai-ee! It is not that."

Balboa looked around helplessly. If only Luaia were near! But he remembered that she had gone to pay a visit to Juan de Caicedo's wife.

"What then?" he asked gruffly. "Why do you weep?"

"My heart," she sobbed, "is twisted like a young tree in a storm of winds." She lifted her swollen face, gulping. "I have a brother, master."

"But surely that is nothing to weep about."

She moaned. "Aye, but he loves me dearly."

"But that is a fine thing," said Balboa, mystified.

Her chin quivered. "But my brother does not love you."

"Many do not." He smiled down at her indulgently. "Do not let it grieve you."

He turned to climb into the saddle, but she ran forward to grip him about the knees.

"Do not go, master! Behold, the entire settlement is in danger. My brother has told me of a plot to destroy every Spaniard in it!"

Balboa stared down at her. "A plot," he said slowly. "A plot to destroy the settlement, you say?" He put a hand down to lift her up.

"Aye, master." She trembled.

"Tell me everything," he commanded sharply.

Five caciques, she told him, had banded together to take the Spanish colony by surprise. Five thousand Indian warriors were ready to attack. They had over a hundred war canoes and a large store of provisions. All was in readiness and the day was drawing near.

"Is this indeed the truth?" asked Balboa, but in his heart he did not doubt. "How have you heard of it?"

"My brother visits me at night," she said. "He is one of the slaves who escaped during the hurricane, master." Her head bent sorrowfully. "He told me this, that I might flee on the appointed day and so escape being slain in the confusion. Ai-ee, master! For telling you this, he will hate me forever."

"Then why," asked Balboa wonderingly, "why have you told?"

"Once," she said humbly, "you saved my life. Also, you spared me from the wrath of Señor Hurtado." She raised dark wet eyes to his face. "I could not see you killed, master."

He put a warm hand on her shoulder. "I am grateful, Fulvia. You shall be rewarded. What will you have?"

"The life of my brother," she wailed. "Spare him, master!"

"I promise."

Fulvia sent for her brother then. Unsuspecting, he came that very night. Captured, he confessed everything. Aye, it was his cacique, Cemaco, who had waylaid Hurtado's men on the Rio Negro. Not only that, but the thirty Indians sent by Cemaco, supposedly as an act of friendship, had in reality been commanded to slay Balboa. But he had always come among them in the fields mounted on his great mare, armed with his formidable spear, so they had not dared attack him with their agricultural tools.

With the Indian youth as guide, the Spaniards set out for the village of Tichiri where the native army was encamped. Seventy went by land, under the leadership of Balboa, and sixty by water, led by Rodrigo de Colmenares.

The colonists fell upon the assembled Indians in the dead of night, slaying and capturing nearly all. The victory was so complete that the surviving natives were filled with dread of these mailclad, supernatural warriors with their demon dogs.

The provisions which the Spaniards were able to seize were a blessing, indeed. They reveled in the unexpected plenty, and their spirits rose. Abundance enough to carry them over until their crops were harvested!

When Balboa returned with his men, all Darien celebrated. Friends and enemies rejoiced, ate and drank together. Differences were, for a few glorious days, forgotten. Balboa was the hero of the moment. Had he not saved the settlement?

Balboa's heart swelled with hope. Perhaps this meant the end of struggles and factions in the colony. Perhaps, at last, they would all be able to work together in harmony for the common good. Had the tide turned? Were the worst days over? Was peace ahead for Darien — and for him?

He stood in the plaza, his arm about Luaia, and listened to the people cheering him. His eyes went over all the friendly faces. His ears heard gratefully the admiring shouts. A little

later, there was to be a banquet, but now this was all the food
he wanted, completely satisfying.

Night enfolded the settlement. Men lit flares and marched
around the square singing. Overhead, stars winked down from
a clear sky and the moon rolled up, full and red in the east.
The tropical breeze, stirring against Balboa's cheek, was soft
and soothing.

"The stars are brilliant tonight," said someone at his elbow.

Balboa turned. Beside him stood Micer Codro, a Venetian
astrologer, lately arrived from Santo Domingo. The man was
slight of stature and slow of speech. It was difficult to become
acquainted with him, for his eyes had a way of drifting past
one, as though more attracted by the unknown than the known.
He claimed to have predicted the deaths of Columbus and
Queen Isabella and to have forecast the fate of many other
notables. He claimed positively that the unfortunate Nicuesa
had drowned at sea and all with him in the ship. Balboa had
spoken with him once regarding his father whose book on the
subject of astrology Micer Codro professed to admire.

"Aye, the heavens sparkle," said Balboa pleasantly. He
laughed. "I suppose, Micer Codro, you read more than mere
beauty aloft, do you not?"

"True," said the other softly. "The sky is a great book to
me, ever fascinating, because ever changing."

"And the stars are the words, I presume," said Balboa, "written in light on the pages of heaven." He chuckled. "'Tis a
fair thought, indeed."

"Aye," responded the astrologer. He lifted a bony arm,
pointing upward. "Behold your star, Vasco Núñez de Balboa."

Balboa's eyes followed Micer Codro's steady finger.

"My star," he said wonderingly. "Have I a star all to
myself?"

"We all have. Yours is a great one."

The star was indeed of surpassing brilliance, flashing sometimes red, sometimes blue-green as Balboa watched, then turning clear-white as a flawless diamond. It seemed to him that it brightened with his eyes upon it, drawing nearer to earth.

Beside him, Luaia breathed softly. "It is beautiful, Vas-co. The finest in the sky."

Balboa wrenched his eyes from it and laughed roughly.

"Now if I could get it down, it would be worth more than all the gold in Terra Firma, would it not, Micer Codro?"

The Venetian appeared not to have heard. His narrow face was still upturned. He spoke dreamily. "Yours is a star of achievement, Vasco Núñez de Balboa. I have traced its course on my charts. Fame will be yours, but peril as well."

"I am well acquainted with peril," scoffed Balboa.

"Hush," said Luaia, her eyes steadfast on the astrologer. "Let him tell more. Verily, I think he is inspired."

Micer Codro's arm moved as though he drew an imaginary line across the heavens. "When your star reaches that point in the heavens, beware, Vasco Núñez de Balboa. That will be a time of greatest peril. Should you survive, however, you will become rich and powerful — the strongest captain in these lands."

Reluctantly impressed by the certainty in the man's voice, Balboa again looked upward, marking the star and the position in his mind.

Luaia gave a little cry. "Ai-ee! I am afraid, Vas-co."

Balboa thrust aside his own solemn thoughts to comfort her. "Do not believe such things, Luaia. Micer Codro did not say I should not survive — only that I might not. I have faced death a hundred times, nor have I flinched. Shall I turn coward now?"

He turned toward the astrologer, but the man had slipped away in the crowd.

Balboa shrugged. "It is time for the banquet, Luaia. Come. Do not be downcast. I verily believe that a man's destiny is ordered by himself, not by the distant stars."

CHAPTER XXIII

GREEN OCTOBER

Autumn had come again. looking back upon the year that had passed, it seemed incredible to Balboa that no more than twelve months had been marked off on his calendar.

It was now October, 1512. In faraway Spain the countryside would be gold and yellow at this season. Peasants were beginning to look forward to the winter festivals. They were busy storing away the crops and all the roads to the towns and villages were ringing with the iron-bound wheels of produce carts. There would be special services in the churches also, and gay parties, and the smell of frost high up along the slopes of the hills.

Gold and yellow in the highlands of Estremadura, his home province — but here, in fall, winter or spring the land was always green, the everlasting changeless green of the tropics. At times, when the memories of those old scenes were most poignant, resentment stirred in him against this implacable land and its green banners. Except for the sea and the white shining peaks of the mountains, there was the one dominant color everywhere, the same sinister motif. Members of the expedition had come to fear it. Or, perhaps, hate it. Green! Vines and brush and trees. Moss dripping with moisture. Shoulder-high grass filling the swamps. Even many of the insects and snakes were green. No eye could escape it; against the changing seasons themselves it was invulnerable.

So had come again another green October. Perhaps, thought

Balboa, he would not have minded it so much if things had gone well. If only he might hear from Zamudio and learn that the Spanish court was sending aid. If only Valdivia might return with good news from Santo Domingo. If only somehow — and quickly — Fortune would turn.

Zamudio had been away more than a year and Valdivia ten months. Yet it had seemed even longer. He was especially anxious about the long absence of Juan de Valdivia. Fifteen thousand castellanos had his friend taken with him as a gift to the authorities in Española. In addition to the gold, he had borne the great news of the new ocean on the other side of the isthmus. Surely that, if nothing else, should have fired the minds of the governor and his council. And the further revelations of the vast empire to the south, richer than the Indies, undoubtedly must have stirred their imaginations with the possibilities of the proposed tour of discovery, exploration and conquest.

Yet nothing had been heard from them. The green jungle days wore on, steaming and hot, and the nights fluttered black wings through intolerable stillness. What had happened? More and more alone with himself and his thoughts, Balboa sat and pondered that question, or paced the floor, his impatience mounting. Could it be that men had lost their valor and initiative? Were they growing soft and womanly? Had they become so engrossed in their petty quarrels and commonplace affairs that they no longer cared to meet the challenge of the unknown? Ah, if he were alive today, the great admiral, Christopher Columbus, would be ashamed of a son so timorous and unprogressive!

Balboa had formed the habit of going each day to the harbor and peering through his telescope for long minutes in hope of sighting a sail. That habit persisted. It had grown upon him to such an extent of late that he was spending most of his leisure time there, silently contemplating the white-capped breakers of the Caribbean and finding in the solemn pounding of the surf an answer to his own spirit's call.

On one of these occasions, instead of proceeding on his lone walk along the sweeping area of the shore, he fell to contemplating the leaky old hull at anchor in the harbor. It was his one remaining caravel, the last ship belonging to the expedition. It rode there like a hope abandoned, a symbol of all the futility and discouragement and despair of the colony. It had been abandoned as useless more than six months ago. Yet, for some reason, no one had thought of destroying it. Perhaps because it was a reminder of better days, or perhaps because, though unseaworthy, it was still something to look at when the thought of their isolation bore too heavily upon them.

Seeing the vessel there, idly creaking in the combers, her mast bleak against the sky, an idea suddenly came to Balboa. Why not recondition her? It might be possible. She had been stripped of her sails and all nautical gear of use to other vessels. But she still had a hull to work on and surely, with ingenuity, a few clever shipwrights and carpenters could improvise a rigging. Rope could be braided or woven from bark. There was no pitch available for use in sealing her bottom, nor hemp for calking her holes and cracks, but mayhap they could find substitutes. No later than yesterday he remembered having seen gum ooze from tree trunks in the jungle. They might use that, or find something even better. He would begin work at once.

Mysteriously his despondency left him. A plan took form. When this ship had been made seaworthy he would himself embark upon her and set sail for Spain. Why leave to a subordinate the task of winning the favor of the court? Zamudio apparently had failed him. Valdivia also, his most trusted friend. The right way to get things done was to do them yourself.

His blue eyes bright with earnestness, his red hair and beard flaming about his head and face, Balboa stood before the hurriedly assembled members of his council. To them he appealed for quick action. Their cause could not, he said, be lost if each man would contribute his strength and the gifts of his mind to this new undertaking.

"Bear patiently with me," he concluded, "and we shall find the shining sea to the south and the empire of wealth beyond. I can say to you with confidence that when the king hears from my own lips of all the opportunities and wonders of this new world, he will grant us our every request."

Balboa's sincerity and earnestness had won over his council. The meeting was adjourned. The task of reconditioning the old hull in the harbor was begun that very day. Quickly the work proceeded in spite of the difficulties. The leaks were stopped, ropes manufactured, rigging assembled, sails cut and made ready. Just as the job was nearing completion, a deputation of grave-faced men assembled outside Balboa's hut and called to him to come forth.

Luaia was terrified.

"Vas-co," she sobbed, clinging to him, "something has gone wrong. By the look of their faces, they would do you harm. I—I am afraid!"

"Nay," Balboa said, "I have no fear of them."

Yet he could not help wondering what new trouble had developed. He strode out into their midst, Leonçico at his heels. As Luaia had said, their expressions were not pleasant. They stood in a queer hushed crowd, not glowering at him as men who mutiny, but each looking to the other, no one willing to act as spokesman.

Balboa smiled encouragement and said: "Friends, what would you have of me?"

A soldier, Luis Botello, broke the silence.

"If it please you," he began, "we have come to ask you to abandon your voyage to Spain."

"Never!" thundered Balboa.

Luis Botello, though embarrassed, continued: "We have talked it over and have grave fears concerning what may befall us here in Darien in your absence."

"Nothing will happen," Balboa scoffed. "Are you afraid of your own shadows?"

Botello shook his head. Then he turned to one of the members of Balboa's council. "You can explain much better than I, Fernando."

"Aye," responded Fernando Múñoz, "I can explain. This colony must endure somehow until aid comes. The ship is ready and that aid must be sent for, we agree. A year, possibly more, must elapse before a ship can return. You, and you alone, the natives of Terra Firma fear and respect. Recent events have convinced us of that."

"But — "

"The moment you depart," went on Múñoz stubbornly, "they will not hesitate to attack the settlement in force and we shall all be annihilated."

"Nay," said Balboa, "I do not believe — "

He paused and glanced toward the caravel, now riding proudly in the harbor and he knew then, heavily reluctant, that he would never cross the ocean in her to Seville. His men were right. He alone had the key to safety in his possession, the power to maintain the peace where others would fail. The alliance he had made with the natives, their wholesome fear of him and, finally, his marriage to the Indian princess, Careta's daughter — all these were guarantees of safety too strong to be ignored.

For the first time in months, Balboa found himself at a loss, like a schoolboy, his face flushed and his manner embarrassed. Like a schoolboy, too, he had difficulty in persuading himself to forego the excitement and high adventure of that voyage.

With an effort he cleared his throat. "I find reason in what you say," he admitted, "but who shall carry our cause to the king?"

Fernando Múñoz spoke again. "We have given it much thought. Rodrigo de Colmenares, your own trusted lieutenant, would do for one, we believe. Then there is that very admirable cavalier, Juan de Caicedo. Both are willing to go and will acquit themselves with credit, if you but say the word."

Balboa turned away. There was a choking in his throat and his hands were actually shaking. How much, how very much he had wanted to go himself! Only he and the understanding Luaia would ever know. Yet fate had intervened, and it was well, perhaps, that she had, for, at all costs, this colony must be maintained. By preserving it, the great work of extending Spanish dominion and glorifying the Spanish name would go on. A new sea was to be charted and a new land discovered. Riches and power beyond the dreams of men were to be gained. Soon, very soon, an expedition would set out toward the fabulous ocean to the south. Here again fate had decreed, and had chosen him for an ally.

Once more he raised his eyes toward those lofty peaks and that green wall of jungle. Then resolutely he swung about, facing his men.

"Dispatch the ship immediately at the tide's turning," he said. "You have chosen well. Colmenares and Caicedo shall represent us at the court of Spain."

CHAPTER XXIV

THE TROUBLEMAKERS AGAIN

WITH RODRIGO DE COLMENARES GONE, BALBOA FELT MUCH ALONE. These were restless men with whom he had to deal, easily aroused and quick either to approve or resent. The food supply was diminishing and with it the comparative concord of the last few weeks. He was not long in realizing that once again envious factions were rising against him.

The growing arrogance of Bartolomé Hurtado was responsible for some of the unrest. Daily he grew more oppressive and boastful, using his long friendship with Vasco Núñez de Balboa both as a sword to cut his own way and as a shield to protect his overbearing conduct from criticism. All the while he maintained an attitude of jealous loyalty to Balboa, taking swift exception to any word of condemnation, dueling at the slightest provocation.

This almost childish adherence was embarrassing to Balboa. When he attempted to suggest to Hurtado that it was doing him more harm than good, the latter sulked.

"I was only acting in your interests as a friend," said Hurtado. "I should think you would reprimand your enemies, instead of your friends, Vasco Núñez. Of course, if you do not value my devotion —"

"But I do value it," protested Balboa. "It's only that your — your extreme fidelity has begun to make enemies for you, as well as for myself."

"For me?" Hurtado knotted his thick eyebrows, his eyes astonished. "Why should I have any enemies?"

"I have been trying to explain," said Balboa patiently. "You are too impulsive. Too ready to exaggerate any insult or disapproval of my actions. Too ready to fly — "

"Well, in that case, surely I can expect your protection, since it is because of you I have gained these enemies," said Hurtado, blustering confidently.

It was no use reasoning with him, Balboa saw, and he gave it up. Lonely as he was, even Hurtado's irrational allegiance touched him. Indeed, was not Bartolomé Hurtado the last old friend left in Darien, with the exception of Andrés Garavito who kept much to himself?

Even as he thought of Andrés, he saw him coming toward him.

"Vasco Núñez!"

"Aye." Balboa paused. It was the first time Andrés Garavito had approached him since Balboa had taken Luaia as wife. Several times Balboa had shown favors to his old shipmate, but Garavito had paid scant heed to his overtures. Now, however, he looked less unfriendly.

"I must see you in private," he said. "Where can we go?"

"To my cabin," said Balboa promptly. "Come."

Luaia rose, startled, as they entered, then brushed by them without a word. Balboa closed the door behind her, and turned to Garavito.

A flush colored the man's face, but it died away as he began to speak.

"There is a plot against Bartolomé Hurtado afoot," he said. "Some of them plan to seize him and lock him up in the jail."

"Who?"

"They are led by Juan Pérez who has been encouraged by Diego del Corral, the lawyer."

"These lawyers!" exclaimed Balboa. His eyes narrowed in disgust.

"Francisco Benítez is with them, too."

"Ah. He bears me a grudge, I hear, for the whipping I gave him because of Nicuesa."

"Aye. And there is Gonzalo Badajoz, the man Nicuesa left in charge of his men at Nombre de Dios when he himself came to Darien."

Balboa nodded. "I suppose he considers himself more entitled to rule Darien, because of that. Well, alone, he is not much of a man to fear. Corral and Pérez are the real rascals."

"I agree." Andrés Garavito leaned closer. "Take my advice and put down this revolt at once, before they have a chance to seize Bartolomé."

"Aye, I suppose you are right. 'Tis an insolent scheme. After all, I am in authority here."

"True. If they imprison your lieutenant, Vasco Núñez, your power will be undermined. Perhaps next — "

"Next they may try to seize me!" Balboa banged the table with his fist. "By heaven, I 'll put a stop to this!" He turned to Garavito. "Thank you for informing me of this, Andrés. You have proved your faithfulness."

Garavito gripped Balboa's outstretched hand, his crafty eyes pleased.

"I told Corral his plan would not work, but he sneered, insinuating that if their conspiracy succeeded I should see what happened to admirers of Vasco Núñez de Balboa!" He rubbed his hands. "Now we shall see who is the strongest!"

Balboa gave him a long level look. "Then you betrayed them

not because of friendship for me, but because you believed their plot would fail."

"For both reasons," replied Garavito hastily. "I was influenced, I assure you, by both my head and my heart."

Balboa turned, disillusioned. Self-interest had led Andrés Garavito hither, but thus were most of the men of Darien governed. Disappointed though he was, he dared not show his distrust, for it would only make another enemy.

He said dully: "You shall be rewarded, Andrés."

Within the hour, soldiers had arrested Alonzo Pérez and Diego del Corral. Protesting loudly against this indignity, they were thrust into prison.

"As an admirer of Enciso," said Balboa, "you should not scorn his former dwelling, my law-worshiping friends."

"I do scorn it," raged Corral, shaking his fist, "as did the good Enciso, also. I scorn you, too, upstart stowaway! Never fear, I shall not long remain here!"

"Aye, we'll soon trade places," cried Alonzo Pérez. "We have many friends who will not see us treated thus!"

Unfortunately, he had spoken the truth. Arming themselves, the followers of Pérez and Corral rushed to the public square, ready to do battle. Balboa's adherents likewise arrayed themselves, led by the hotheaded Bartolomé Hurtado himself, his whole body proclaiming defiance.

Not realizing that civil strife was imminent, Balboa had gone off to the woods to hunt when a group of colonists came after him, shouting news of the latest developments.

Among them was a former follower of Nicuesa, a certain Hernando de Argüello. From the first, he had been friendly to Balboa and eager to support him.

Now he begged Balboa to return to the settlement.

"Any moment now these fiery-hearted stupids may come to

blows," he declared anxiously. "Once started, a war will not
end until both victor and victim come to grief."

"That is true, Hernando," said Balboa. "No matter which
side wins, many will be killed, and finally we shall be prey to
the hostile natives."

He returned therefore in haste to the public square.

Seeing him, his followers shouted hysterically, believing that
he had come to lead them in battle.

Balboa, however, simply took his stand between the two
armies and lifted his hand for attention.

"Men of Darien, what madness is this? Would you slay in
order that you in your turn may be targets for Indian arrows?
Are we not few enough?"

Soldiers on both sides looked abashed and shuffled their feet.
A few voices lifted in behalf of the prisoners, Corral and Pérez.

"I will release these two men," cried Balboa, "on one condition. Let these disturbances cease."

After a noisy argument, the followers of Corral and Pérez
agreed to disperse. The prisoners were freed, outwardly somewhat chastened but inwardly still rebellious.

Within a short time they again roused many of the settlers,
not against Bartolomé Hurtado this time but Balboa himself.

They accused him of unfairness in dividing the gold and
slaves taken on recent expeditions. They threatened him with
arrest and trial. They insisted, moreover, that the ten thousand
castellanos in the smelting house be turned over to one of their
own choice for immediate division.

Seeing that argument was useless and merely served to arouse
further opposition, Balboa turned on his heel and left the
throng.

In the cabin Luaia was waiting anxiously.

"Vas-co, I am so worried. You are safe?"

He nodded grimly. "I am safe, but I am wearied of it all. I am going hunting. The woods are quiet."

Some of his friends followed, amazed to find that he was going on a hunting trip at such a critical time.

"Do you not realize what will happen if you leave the settlement at such a time?" protested Hernando de Argüello.

"Aye," cried Fernando Múñoz, "Pérez and Corral will seize command — "

"Very likely," said Balboa calmly.

"But then they will take the ten thousand castellanos and divide them while you are gone," said Luis Botello.

"I suppose they will."

"And when you return they will try to throw you into prison," warned Andrés Garavito.

"Are you going to abandon yourself and your friends to the revenge of these unscrupulous troublemakers?" cried Bartolomé Hurtado.

"Not at all."

"Then you will remain?" asked Argüello.

"No." He thrust his hand through his disordered thatch of red hair. "I am going hunting. I shall be gone overnight. Perhaps for a day or two."

"But — "

"If any of you care to come with me, I shall be glad to have your company." His blue eyes, smiling and friendly, went from one to the other searchingly.

" 'Tis madness," said Luis Botello glumly at last, "but I 'll come."

"I 'm a madman, too," said Fernando Múñoz.

"I have no taste to see what must surely happen here in the village. I 'll go with you," said Hernando de Argüello.

"And I," said Bartolomé Hurtado, "though I would sooner stay and fight it out."

Only Andrés Garavito elected to remain in the settlement. The others set off pessimistically with Balboa, their faces gloomy, their steps dragging.

Almost out of sight of his cabin, Balboa turned and looked back. He could barely discern his wife's figure standing dejectedly in the doorway. He waved to her. Her own hand fluttered bravely in answer. Balboa set his face toward the jungle, frowning. What if things did not work out as he expected?

Halfway back to the settlement two days later, a messenger from Darien came hastening to meet them. He had come, he said, to beg Vasco Núñez de Balboa to return at once.

"What has happened?" asked Balboa.

"Pérez and Corral seized the government soon after you departed — "

Bartolomé Hurtado turned excitedly to Balboa. "Did I not warn you? I knew that would happen."

Balboa's eyes did not waver from the messenger's face.

"And then — ?"

"They took charge of the ten thousand castellanos and commenced to divide them."

"I told you, Vasco Núñez! I told you!" Hurtado looked bitterly triumphant. "We are lost!"

"Go on," said Balboa.

"They had scarcely begun the division of the gold when dissensions arose," continued the man breathlessly.

"Ah."

"Everyone was dissatisfied. They claimed the shares unequally distributed. They turned against Pérez and Corral. All declared that whereas you had won the treasure through valor and divided it fairly among the deserving, these men had taken it by force to satisfy their own greed."

De Argüello clapped Balboa admiringly on the shoulder. "I understand now. You foresaw what would happen, Vasco Núñez de Balboa! Ah, you are not only a brave soldier, but a wise leader as well."

Returning to Darien they found that the fickle mob had thrown Diego del Corral and Alonzo Pérez into prison. Balboa was hailed by a cheering throng and borne to the plaza on the shoulders of many former followers of Pérez and Corral. It was a signal victory for Balboa and doubly gratifying because it had been obtained by the use of intelligence rather than force.

Food supply was becoming a problem again, however, and it was with great joy that the colonists welcomed two ships which arrived from Isla Española the first of the year. In command of these vessels was Captain Cristóbal Serrano and he brought a cargo of provisions and two hundred men. They had come in response to the urging of Juan de Valdivia a year and a half before.

Captain Serrano brought for Balboa a royal commission from the treasurer of Isla Española, appointing him Captain-general of Antigua. Even while gratitude swelled in Balboa that at last he had full authority over the colony, another letter was handed to him.

It was from Zamudio and as he read Balboa went from happiness to deep despair.

CHAPTER XXV

BALBOA WRITES A LETTER TO HIS KING

THE EXCITEMENT OF THE SHIPS' ARRIVAL BRINGING THE CARGO OF supplies and reinforcements was not soon over. The two hundred men had marched to the plaza to be assigned to billets, the cargo had been put ashore, Balboa had escorted Captain Cristóbal Serrano to his house where he was to be a guest for the night, and then, carrying in one hand his royal commission as captain-general of the colony and, in the other, Zamudio's disheartening letter, Vasco Núñez de Balboa sought the privacy of his own room.

How much he needed to be alone!

Bitterness and a feeling of frustration were his this night, when everywhere throughout the little colony were rejoicing and prayers and feasting. From his window he could see the beach, near the quay, illuminated with campfires. The plaza itself was gay with chatting soldiers and singing groups of men, carrying torches. Near at hand, the music of an accordion could be heard. Suddenly, to express the exuberance and hilarity of the colonists, a cannon was fired from one of the ships, its echo roaring up among the dark crags of the nearby mountains.

The occasion was being fittingly celebrated, Balboa thought, and tried to smile. But across his worn, unhappy face, there passed only another shadow. Candlelight fell over his bowed head. He was rereading the letter from Zamudio. The hurt it had brought him was deep, becoming almost impossible to bear. If he could have wept, that would have helped. But instead, he must suffer unshed tears, know the greatest disappointment that had ever come to him in the lines of a letter. Zamudio had failed. Enciso had won. A new governor, it was rumored, was coming out to the colony. At this moment Zamudio was in hiding and feared for his very life. Smooth oratory, covering Enciso's deceit and treachery, had prejudiced the king and the court against Zamudio. By a royal decree His Majesty would soon write "finis" to a career that had progressed to a place where success would soon have crowned it with gold and glory.

It was hard to believe that the warning conveyed to Balboa by his partner in Spain was genuine. How could it be real when even the New World seemed to reveal the signs of a just God? Yet Zamudio, a true friend, had written that he should be on guard, for it was rumored that immediately upon the arrival of the new governor he, Vasco Núñez, would be arrested. Even more astonishing, he would be placed on trial for the murder of Nicuesa. For the murder of Nicuesa! Nicuesa, it seemed, had never arrived in Española. He had gone down, with all hands, to the bottom of the sea. And though he, Balboa, had had no part in it and could face his prosecutors with a clear conscience, they could upon the black word of such a man as Martin Fernández de Enciso send him to his death.

Perspiration stood out upon his forehead. This was the agony he must bear while the rest of the colonists were abandoning themselves to the joy of being delivered from hunger and despair. Now, down along the beach or in the plaza, wherever they foregathered, men would be discussing the forthcoming expedition to the South Sea. Hope would blaze forth anew. There would be tall tales tonight of temples of gold and streets of emerald, of the beautiful veiled women of the East, of camel trains bearing spices and incense and precious silks along the caravan routes from Cathay.

Aye, the golden Indies lying along the shores of that southern ocean would be the subject tonight of all their talk. This was as it should be, of course. And except for the blasting news and warning of that letter, he would be with them himself, drinking a toast to the king and regaling them with his own version of the story. Probably if King Ferdinand had known of all these wonderful things, he would not now be sending out a new governor to Darien to replace him.

Luaia had entered the room quietly. Balboa looked up to find her there, a lovely figure in white. But her eyes were very sad. He knew instantly that she had guessed something was wrong.

"Vas-co," she said, "why do you not go out to rejoice with your men?"

"I cannot."

"And why?"

"My king has turned against me because of Enciso's lying tongue."

"You should have gone yourself, Vas-co."

Balboa suppressed a groan. "It is too late."

But she would not believe it. She, if not the king, had faith in her lord, knew the depth of him, felt his greatness.

Presently she said: "Vas-co, why do you not write a letter to your great cacique, explaining all. He will believe you."

Such a thing had not occurred to Balboa, but immediately he saw the possibility for success. Aye, he would write a letter, as full a letter as man had ever written to his king. He would clarify his position, deny Enciso's charges. But, above all, he would impress upon his majesty the urgency of sending troops and provisions quickly for the expedition to the southern ocean.

Hopeful once more and burning with the desire to vindicate himself, Balboa stooped and kissed the face of his little Indian princess.

"My dear," he said, "you have spoken well. I will do it. One of the two ships arrived today shall bear my letter across the sea to Spain."

With his wife sitting near, Balboa began to write, his face lined and earnest in the wavering candlelight, his fingers tight upon his quill.

I desire to give an account to your most Royal Highness of the great secrets and marvellous riches of this land of which God has made your most Royal Highness the Lord and me the discoverer before any other, for which I give many thanks and much praise for all the days of the world, and I hold myself to be the most fortunate man that has been born in the world, seeing that our Lord has been served at my hands rather than at those of another. As so propitious a commencement has been made, I beseech your most Royal Highness that I may be permitted to complete this great enterprise, and I am bold enough to make this supplication to your most Royal Highness because I know that you will thus be well served, for I venture to say that with the help of God and with industry I shall be able to conduct the enterprise in such a way that your most Royal Highness will thereby be well served. . .

Lines of concentration deepened in his forehead as he wrote, but the scratching of the pen was somehow soothing to his troubled spirit. Now and again, pausing for thought and to rest his cramped fingers, he glanced toward Luaia. Her smile came quickly, sweet with encouragement and pride in him, but she did not speak nor intrude in any way upon the task he labored at.

The nature of this land is such that if he who has charge of the government sleeps, he cannot wake when he wishes, for this is a land that obliges the man who governs to be very watchful. The country is difficult to travel through, on account of the numerous rivers, morasses and mountains, where many men die owing to the great labor they have to endure, for every day we are exposed to death in a thousand forms. I have thought of nothing, by day or by night, but how to support myself and the handful of men whom God has placed under my charge, and how to maintain them until your Highness sends reinforcements.

I have taken care that the Indians of this land are not ill-treated, permitting no man to injure them, and giving them many things from Castile, whereby they may be drawn into friendship with us. This honorable treatment of the Indians has been the cause of my learning great secrets from them, through the knowledge of which large quantities of gold may be obtained and your highness will thus be well served.

I have often thought how it would be possible for us to sustain life, seeing that we have been as badly succored from the island of Española as if we had not been Christians. But our Lord, by His infinite mercy, has chosen to supply us with provisions in this land, though we have often been in such straits that we expected to die of hunger; yet at the time of our greatest necessity our Lord has pointed out the means of relief. Your most Royal Highness must know that after we came here we were forced to travel from one place to another, by reason of the great scarcity, and it astonishes me how we could have endured such hardships. The things that have happened have been more by the hand of God than by the hand of man.

Up to the present time, I have taken care that none of my people shall go hence unless I myself go in front of them, whether it might be by night or day, marching across rivers, through swamps and forests and over mountains; and your Royal Highness should not imagine that the swamps of this land are so light that they can be crossed easily for many times we have had to go a league, and two or three leagues through swamps and water, stripped naked, with our clothes fastened on a shield above our heads, and when we had come to the end of one swamp we have had to enter another, and to walk in this way from two or three to ten days. And if the person who is entrusted with the government of this land remains in his house and leaves work to others, no one else he can send in his place can manage the people so well, or fail to make mistakes which may cause the destruction of himself and of all who are with him. I can say this with truth, as a person who has seen what happens; for sometimes, when I have been unable to go with the men because I have been detained by some business connected with the sowing of the crops, I have observed that those whom I have sent in my place have not acted according to reason.

Someone knocked loudly on the outside door. A dozen merry voices called his name. Balboa motioned abstractedly to Luaia.

"Tell them I cannot join them now. Later, mayhap."

She went out quietly and he bent again over the paper.

I, my Lord, have taken care that everything that has been obtained up to the present day shall be properly divided, as well the gold and pearls (the share of your most Royal Highness being put on one side) as the clothing and eatables; but up to the present time we have valued the eatables more than the gold, for we have more gold than health, and often have I searched in various directions, desiring more to find a sack of corn than a bag of gold; and I can certify the truth of this to your most Royal Highness, for we have been more in want of food than of gold. I assure your most Royal Highness that if I had not personally gone in front of my men, searching for food for those who went with me as well as for those that remained in this town, there would have been no one left in the town or in the land, unless our Lord had miraculously taken pity upon us. . .

Luaia had hardly returned when more heavy knocks fell on the door. Balboa himself rose this time to see who it was, determined to set a guard hereafter so that he might not further be disturbed.

Andrés Garavito stood without.

"I have come to suggest that those in the jail be released," he said. "Many cry for their freedom, Vasco Núñez, and if you liberated them, your own popularity would increase, rather than suffer."

"Aye, set them free!" said Balboa, instantly generous. "They had escaped my mind, Andrés. Go, give the order!"

As he sat down to write again, he sighed.

Perhaps he had done wrong to free Diego del Corral and his minions. He was as troublesome as that other lawyer, Enciso, continually harassing the peace of the struggling colony. He took up his quill, frowning.

Most puissant Lord, I desire to ask a favor of your Highness, for I have done much in your service. It is that your Highness will command that no Bachelor of Laws nor of anything else, unless it be of medicine, shall come to this part of the Indies on pain of heavy punishment which your Highness shall order to be inflicted, for no bachelor has ever come here who is not a devil, and who does not lead the life of devils. And not only are they themselves evil, but they give rise to a thousand lawsuits and quarrels. This order will be greatly to the advantage of your Highness' service, for the country is new. . .

He sat staring into the shadows, sifting memories and facts in his mind before continuing. The noise and laughter drifting to him from the festive colonists impressed his thoughts but faintly. Carefully he selected the information which his king might find most interesting and valuable.

That which I, by much labor and great hardships, have been able to discover, is as follows: In this province of Darien many rich mines have been found, and there is gold in great quantities. . . Following the course of the great river San Juan (or Darien or Atrato, as it has been variously called) for thirty leagues on the right hand side, one arrives at a province called Abanumaque, which contains much gold. . . Thirty leagues up this great river on the left hand, a very large and beautiful stream flows into it, and two days' journey up this stream there is a cacique called Davaive. . . All the gold that goes forth from this gulf comes from the house of the Cacique Davaive, as well as all that is owned by the caciques of those districts, and it is reported that they have many pieces of gold curiously worked, and very large. Many Indians who have seen them tell me that this Cacique Davaive has certain bags of gold, and that it takes the whole strength of a man to lift one of them on his back. . .

There are two methods of collecting the gold without any trouble. One is by waiting until the river rises in the ravines, and when the freshets pass off, the beds remain dry, and the gold is laid bare which has been robbed from the mountains and brought down in very large lumps. The Indians describe them as being the size of oranges or of a fist, and others like flat slabs. The other way of gathering gold is by waiting until the plants on the hills are dry, which are set on fire, and when they are consumed the Indians go to search in the most likely places and collect great quantities of very beautiful grains of gold. The Indians who gather this gold bring it in grains to be melted and barter it with this Cacique Davaive in exchange for youths and boys to eat, and for women to serve them as wives, whom they do not eat. . . This Cacique Davaive has a great place for melting gold in his house and he has a hundred men continually working at the gold. I know all this of a certainty, for I have never received any other account in whatever direction I may have gone. I have heard it from many caciques and Indians. . .

That which is to be found down this coast to the westward is the province called Coyba, which is twenty leagues distant. . . Further down the coast, at a distance of forty leagues from this city and twelve leagues inland, there is a cacique named Comogre and another named Pocorosa. . . At the distance of a day's journey from the Cacique Pocorosa's house there are the most beautiful mountains that have been seen in these parts. . . In these mountains there are certain caciques who have great quantities of gold in their houses. It is said that these caciques store their gold in *barbacoas* like maize, because it is so abundant that they do not care to keep it in baskets; that all the rivers in these mountains contain gold; and that they have very large lumps in great abundance. Their method of collecting the gold is by going into the water and gathering it in their baskets. They also scrape it up in the beds of streams, when they are dry; and that your most Royal Highness may be more completely informed concerning these parts, I send an Indian workman of that district who has collected it many times. . .

I, Sire, have myself been very near these mountains, within a day's journey, but I did not reach them because I was unable to do so, owing to the want of men; for a man gets as far as he can, not as far as he wishes. Beyond these mountains the country is very flat toward the south, and the Indians say that the other sea is at a distance of three days' journey. All the caciques and Indians of the country of Comogre tell me that there is such great store of gold collected in lumps in the houses of the caciques of the other sea, that we should be astonished... They say that the people of the other coast are very good and well-mannered; and I am told that the other sea is very good for canoe navigation, for that it is always smooth, and never rough like the sea on this side, according to the Indians. I believe that there are many islands in that sea. They say that there are many large pearls, and that the caciques have baskets of them, as well as the Indian men and women generally.

It is a most astonishing thing and without equal that our Lord has made you the Lord of this land. It should not be forgotten that your most Royal Highness will be served by sending me reinforcements; when I will, if our Lord favors me, discover things so grand and places where so much gold and such wealth may be had that a greater part of the world might be conquered with it. I assure your Royal Highness that I have worked with more diligence for the service of your most Royal Highness than the governors who were lost here, Alonso de Ojeda and Diego de Nicuesa; for I have not remained in my bed while my people were entering and exploring the country. I must let your most Royal Highness know that no party has gone into any part of this land unless I was in front as a guide opening the road with my own hands for those who went with me.

As one who has seen the things of these parts and who has more knowledge of the land than anyone else has hitherto acquired, and because I desire that the affairs of these regions which I have originated may flourish and reach such a position as to be of service to your most Royal Highness, I must make known what is necessary to be done and to be provided at once and until the land is known and explored. The chief requirement is that a thousand men should come from the Island of Española, for those who might come direct from Castile would not be fit for much until they were accustomed to the country, for they would be lost and us who are now here with them. Your most Royal Highness will please to order that for the present this colony be supplied with provisions at the hand of your most Royal Highness, that the land may be explored and its secrets made known. And thus two things will be effected: one that much money will be gained in the markets, and the other and principal one that, the land being supplied with provisions, great things and vast riches may be discovered by the help of God.

It is also necessary to provide the means of building small ships for the rivers, and to send pitch, nails, ropes and sails with some master shipwrights who understand ship-building. Your most Royal Highness should also send two hundred crossbows with very strong stays and fittings and with long ranges. They should not weigh more than two pounds, and money would thus be saved, because each man in this place ought to have one or two crossbows, as they are very good arms against the Indians, and useful in the chase of birds and other game. Two dozen very good hand guns, of light metal, are also required, for those made of iron are soon damaged by the constant damp, and are eaten away with rust. They should not weigh more than from twenty-five to thirty pounds, and they should not be long, so that a man may be able to carry one of them wherever it may be necessary. Very good powder is also wanted. . . What I should urge, most puissant Lord, is that people should come, so that the land may be explored from these two stations of Davaive and Comogre, and that the secrets of it may be known, as well as those of the sea on the other side towards the south, and all other matters. And if your Highness would command that everything should be supplied which I have asked for, it would be a great advantage, and the land would be provided with everything that is necessary. Your Highness should receive all this from me as your loyal servant, and should give it credence because your Highness' service will thus be advanced. I do not desire to make towers of wind like the governors whom your Highness sent out, for between them both they have lost eight hundred men, and those whom I have rescued scarcely amount to fifty, and this is the truth. Your Highness will consider all that I have done and discovered and endured with these people, without any help but from God and my own industry.

Balboa stopped to wipe the perspiration from his face and to shoo away the gnats which swarmed before his eyes and fell, candle-singed, to the letter before him. Truly, this was a most arduous business, this forming of words and phrases calculated to convince. He would far rather have met his monarch face to face and used his tongue to win an understanding. Sentences, clear in the mind, had a way of warping and twisting when set upon the paper. How could he be sure that these crawling black symbols would convey his true message? Ah, for the smooth rhetoric of a man of letters!

He scratched part of what he had written, and doggedly went on again.

If I have erred in anything in working for the service of your Highness, I beseech your Highness that my earnest desire to serve your Highness may be considered. Although, most puissant Lord, I have not succeeded in doing all that is necessary in this land, I can certify that I know how to administer better than all those who have come here hitherto; and that your Highness may understand this, you must consider how little other governors have discovered until today, and how they all have failed, and left these shores very full of graves, while, although many Christians lie underground, it is true that most of those that have died have been eaten by dogs and crows. I do not desire to enlarge upon this, but your Highness should know what each man has been able to do and has done up to this time.

Most puissant Lord — I have sent Sebastian del Campo that your Highness may be better informed of all that has passed here; and I entreat your Highness to give him full credence, for he has been informed by me of the whole truth concerning all that can be done in the service of your Highness, and of that which ought to be done in this land. . . In a brigantine that we sent from here, on board of which was Juan de Caicedo and Rodrigo de Colmenares, I forwarded to your Highness 500 pesos of gold from the mines, in very beautiful grains,—and as the voyage is somewhat dangerous for small vessels, I now send to your Highness, by Sebastian del Campo, 370 pesos of gold from the mines. I would have sent more if it had not been for the impossibility of collecting it during the short time the vessels were here. With respect to all that I have said, I beseech your Highness to do that which is best for your service. May the life and royal estate of your Highness prosper by the addition of many more kingdoms and lordships to your sacred rule, and may all that is discovered in these parts increase the power of your Highness as your most Royal Highness may desire, for there are greater riches here than in any other part of the world.

From the town of Santa María del Antigua, in the province of Darien, in the gulf of the Urabá, today this Thursday the 20th of January in the year 1513. The making and creation of your Highness, who kisses your most royal hands and feet, Vasco Núñez de Balboa.

It was nearly dawn when the pen fell from Balboa's aching fingers. More exhausted than if he had taken a ten days' march through swamp and jungle, he lowered his head on his arms and slept.

Luaia had long since succumbed to huddled uncomfortable slumber. The little candle, shrunken into nothing, gasped once and left the room to darkness.

CHAPTER XXVI

WATCHTOWER FOR THE SOUTHERN SEA

ONE EVENING LATE IN THE SUMMER OF 1513 BALBOA "WALKED IN the prolonged quiet of his thoughts" and suddenly came to a decision.

So much waiting had worn down his patience. He neither slept nor ate well. Worry had put marks upon his face. His great muscular frame had thinned. His eyes, though still a piercing blue, no longer held that look of restless interest which men had observed there only a few short years before.

He was a changed man. Not changed, however, in the manner of Hurtado, his former close friend, nor of Nicuesa, the unfortunate. Nor like Pizarro, who had come out from Spain laughing and light hearted, to grow, under the pressure of events, a silent and ruthless soldier. No, the change in Balboa, by some remarkable process, had taken from him none of his humanitarian qualities. Instead of growing harder in his relations toward others, he had become more benevolent. He was more devout, more introspective, more deliberate in his actions. He was kinder, too, in ministering to the needs of his men, in caring for the sick and injured — in going out of his way to make the burdens of his fellows easier to bear.

Furthermore, the change had not affected his courage. He was, without question, the most valorous man in the colony, even braver in adversity than in victory. And now, with the sense of defeat growing hourly, he kept his faith and his head high. At this rate, he reasoned, waiting for the succor that never came from Spain, he might never be given the chance to head that expedition to the South Sea nor to behold any of the mysteries on its shores. The kingdoms laden with gold and shining treasure would never be reached by idling here. His men had become lax and undisciplined, weakened by the sedentary life. The stores brought from Santo Domingo were rapidly diminishing — and still no news, no hope from Spain.

He must act quickly. From the roster of names of those in the settlement, he selected one hundred and ninety men, the pick of the lot.

These he summoned to him and said: "You are hardy and experienced, every one, worthy of the great undertaking I have in mind. But it is no light adventure. Truly, you may need to brave death for the glory of our king. Are you willing? Will you go with me to that great ocean spoken of by the son of Comogre?"

For perhaps a full minute, such silence fell upon the gathering that Vasco Núñez might well have imagined he was alone. Then he saw Pizarro's narrow face kindling with slow fire. The face of Andrés de Valderrábano cleared of amazement. Another, Luis Botello, lifted wide eager eyes.

Quickly, the astonishment and consternation which had greeted Balboa's words were gone. Now there rode over the countenance of each man a charging cavalcade of expressions. Bartolomé Hurtado shouted: "What of the thousand men you called for, O Lionhearted? We are but a fifth of that number. Is this a jest?"

"Nay, no jest." Balboa's eyes met Hurtado's steadily. "With God's help, it can be done."

Pizarro's eyes seemed to be burning in his head. He pushed his way forward. Balboa had never beheld such eagerness in him.

"You speak truly. A thousand soldiers from Spain, untrained in the ways of this land, untempered by the hardships we have undergone, would sooner fail than this weathered lot."

"Aye, that is so!" exclaimed several.

Balboa straightened his shoulders.

"Comrades of Darien," he said, "in this hour I have called you for a service the like of which has never before been the privilege of ordinary men. I go to the South Sea or perish in the attempt. Who is with me?"

The answer was clamorous. Every man volunteered. Not a single voice demurred. Balboa's throat tightened at the prolonged and noisy ovation they gave him.

They dispersed, at his command, to make ready for the journey. From the arsenal, swords, shields, crossbows and arquebuses were selected. Dogs of war, including Balboa's own scarred veteran, Leonçico, were put on leash and taken to the compound to await embarkation. One of the ships in the harbor was stocked with provisions. Later, ten canoes were brought aboard and a sufficient number of natives to man them and also to act as servants for the expedition.

Then, without further preliminary, Balboa explained his plan. By sea they would follow the coast to Careta's province, landing at Aclá in Coyba. From Aclá, they would secure native guides and porters for the first lap of the journey to the cacique Ponca's domain. From there, he understood, the route to the mysterious ocean led southward through the mountainous province of Quarequa. Here ruled Torecha, a native prince, who carried on relentless warfare against all his neighbors to the north. Being his closest neighbor, Ponca had to fight him continuously and bore most of the brunt of that savage chieftain's wrath.

How far from Torecha's territory lay the ocean, Balboa was

not sure. But they would find out in due course. God would make all things known to them. They must place themselves in His hands, work together, and have infinite patience and courage. Above all, it would be absolutely necessary to make friends of all the natives along the route. They were traveling with such heavy armor and equipment that it would be impossible to take food. They must depend upon the natives for that.

On September 1, to the accompaniment of cheers and the roar of a cannon, the ship sailed out of the harbor of Darien. The Caribbean was smoking with the blue haze of late summer and they rode through gentle swells before a favorable wind.

In four days they reached Aclá, disembarked, left a few men in charge of the ship, and marched immediately to Careta's village. Porters and supplies were secured here and on September 6 the trek southward commenced.

Hourly they toiled through the jungle. Porters, wielding their machetes, hacked away vines and creepers. The rivers they crossed were green tunnels swarming with crocodiles and venomous snakes. Monkeys screeched in protest as they passed. Jaguars followed them in hopes of picking off stragglers. Drinking water was either stinking or brackish. Insects, mosquitos and bats plagued them at every turn.

Hot by day, so hot that the blood of man was as fever in his veins and his heart a thumping weight in his breast. Cold by night with the shivering damp coming out of the ground and the mist struggling wraithlike all about, thick as a blanket. The alternating chill and burning of malaria attacked many, some so severely that they had to be borne on makeshift stretchers.

The jungle grew less dense, the ground softer. Wide-bladed grass of the swamps, shoulder high, stood out in great clumps, then came together in a thick, cutting barricade. There were miles of this — of all the intolerable barriers of the journey, the worst. Sometimes they floundered waist deep in it. Often sinkholes caught the unwary and a man would go, gasping and sputtering, into the bottomless black ooze to his neck before a rescue could be effected.

Balboa, as was his custom, went ahead and the example he set made his comrades respect and admire him. Powerful of physique as were many of the native porters, they could not keep pace with him. Yet he was giving more of his strength than he should, he began to realize. The store was diminishing, his reserve was burning up. The almost constant day and night strain had hollowed out his cheeks and rimmed his eyes with shadows. He was weary almost past endurance on the day the party entered a region of great trees, a valley land, indescribably rich and fertile, and they made their way to the village of the cacique, Ponca.

Arrived in the village Balboa's spirits grew bleak with disappointment. The place was deserted. Not a soul, indoors or out. Not a morsel of food or one vessel of native wine. A few empty gourds littered the ground around the rectangular houses. Here and there upon one of the palm-thatched roofs a buzzard blinked, twisting a long neck to look at them. It was maddening to find turkey feathers and the bones of deer and other game, but no meat. No bread. No vegetables in the ravished gardens.

Francisco Pizarro, moved out of his impassivity, drew a long face and cried: "A curse — aye, a thousand curses upon the fleeing infidels!"

Not one member of the party had eaten that day. Balboa drew in his belt and motioned the natives accompanying them to draw near.

"You are tired," he said, "even as we are. But we can neither eat nor drink until Ponca, the cacique of this village, is found and persuaded to return to the village. I entreat you, therefore, to go out and find him. Offer him our friendship and esteem. Tell him that no harm shall befall him or his people. We come in peace and shall depart in peace."

After a short rest, the native ambassadors disappeared into the forest bearing gifts of bright cloth, hawk bells and mirrors. They were heard from no more that day. The sun was high when they returned, leading a great host of the chieftain's people, Ponca at their head. Perceiving that the embassy had met with success, the Spaniards set up a great shout of joy. Balboa hurried forward to welcome the cacique.

"My men starve," he said. "Thank God you have come."

Ponca apologized for doubting the motives of the Spaniards. He had been under a misapprehension, he said, supposing that Balboa had been marching hither to war upon them. This explained why he had abandoned his village, taking the food supplies with him.

Balboa said: "This is a mission of peace. I go to the southern ocean. I have no quarrel with anyone."

Ponca was so pleased that he presented Balboa with a small quantity of gold, the precious metal which he had heard these strangers greatly loved, and all the food they could eat and carry with them on the journey.

In return Balboa gave Ponca more trinkets, a shirt and an iron hatchet. A fiesta was proclaimed. Following that, the cacique invited Balboa to his house. Here, until long into the night, they talked, swearing eternal friendship. Ponca confided to Balboa that though the way was difficult, it was not unendurable. He gave him explicit directions for the journey and cautioned him to be on guard against the people of Quarequa who were fierce and warlike. These tribes, many of whom dwelt in the mountains, were ruled over by a certain cacique, Torecha. For months now, Torecha had made war upon him, Ponca said, and was exceedingly cruel and barbaric in his treatment of prisoners and slaves.

"If you can escape Torecha's wrath," he concluded, "your chances of reaching the great sea will be good."

On the following morning Vasco Núñez again met Ponca. The servants and porters from Careta's province were then dismissed and sent back with twelve of the Spaniards who were too sick to go any farther, and fresh guides and porters were chosen from among Ponca's men. Already weighted with weapons and heavy armor, the party had to rely almost entirely upon natives to carry the surplus food stores.

Soon they were ready to start. Ponca drew Balboa aside and pointed to a distant mountain peak, now gloriously glinting in the sun.

"From yonder peak the great ocean will be visible." Smiling he shook hands with him, after the manner of the Spaniards. "Fare ye well. I shall be awaiting your safe return."

Balboa took his place at the head of the column: soldiers in armor bearing gleaming shields, dogs snarling and snapping on leash behind them, and the porters, bare to the waist, true men of the wilderness with lean thighs and powerful backs.

Turning, Balboa raised his hand for attention.

"Be ready," he commanded. "March!"

Swords rattled. Feet thundered along the turf. No one looked back. Through the trees along the river Balboa led his men forward once more. But this time the goal was in sight. A majestic mountain, pushing its head skyward above the green furrowed stretches of the jungle, seemed to be shining with glorious promise.

It was the watchtower for the wondrous Southern Sea!

CHAPTER XXVII

"GOD HAS GIVEN ME THIS DAY—"

THE THREE DAYS' MARCH FROM PONCA'S VILLAGE TO TORECHA'S province was slow and tortuous. Heat no longer was tempered by coastal breezes, for mountains ahead and the hills behind were effective barricades. This was a land of innumerable small streams and sudden stretches of morass. In places the country was rugged and broken. Fissures in the rocks often had to be bridged, thorny thickets cut down, precipitous slopes cleared of slippery moss and ooze, before the cavalcade could advance.

Often Balboa thought of the letter he had written to King Ferdinand, and certain words came back to him: "I myself go in front . . . whether it might be by night or day . . . across rivers, through swamps and forests and over mountains . . . through water, stripped naked, with our clothes fastened on a shield above our heads. . ."

He was still going in front, now as always, but never before had he met with so many obstacles nor coped with such conditions. Nature, he thought, had never before assembled at one time and in one place so many devices to make his men miserable and the journey hard. On the first night, the expedition as one man dropped in its tracks, too weary even to think of food. Malaria had broken into the ranks and some were delirious, crying out for water or begging for hot coals to break the chill that froze them. Others sat staring gloomily at bleeding feet or legs swollen with insect bites.

The gloom was like a darkness that flattened over the earth.

It was in the minds of everyone. What cared they for shining new seas and empires to be gained at such a cost? Balboa himself was despondent. His men were suffering and their suffering was his. He could feel the pain of their bleeding feet, their insect bites, and the crushing weight of their despair. And he himself was not well. There had come the recurrence of a slight fever he had experienced a year ago. There were intervals of hot and cold, a dragging lassitude he could not shake off.

"God and Mother Mary!" wailed one of the soldiers. Others joined in the fevered supplication.

Attending the sick as well as he could, Vasco Núñez finally stumbled out beyond the rim of campfire light where he could not be seen, and knelt down to pray. Of late he had prayed oftener than had been his wont. In these vast stilly places he had somehow seemed closer to God. The dark nights were the still nights, for when the moon and stars were bright and the sky clear, the jungle was a bedlam of curious and startling noises: monkeys crying, grouse beating their wings, insects in great swarms dropping from trees so that the sound of them was as spattering rain.

But tonight it was so still that Balboa could hear his own breath, the quiet movements of his dry lips. Presently he rose, crossed himself, and went back with a surer stride to his own crude couch. On the pile of dry river grass he slept soundly until morning.

The second day was worse than the first. Food was running low. Nearly half of the men had malaria. The natives, one by one, were deserting because of the fear they had of the poisoned arrows of the Indians of Quarequa. Two scouts who had reconnoitered ahead of the party returned with the news that Torecha had posted advance guards along the Spanish line of march.

"Harass the hated foreigners," the cacique had said. "Kill as many as you can so that when they arrive it will be easy to exterminate them in a pitched battle."

All that day and the next there were constant attacks from the unseen enemy. Two porters were killed and a Spaniard wounded. Balboa ordered the war dogs loosened, then, that they might seek out the Indians lurking in ambuscade and drive them beyond arrow range. After that, not a single casualty marked the forward progress of his men. By now they had reached the border of Torecha's territory. The way opened before them; ahead were cleared places in the woods and growing gardens. Here and there in groups of three or four were rectangular-shaped two-story houses set near the edge of the plantations. The Spaniards marveled at the fertility of the soil, at the crops grown there, at the park-like beauty of the country.

Their amazement turned to consternation, however, when a bend in the trail brought them face to face with over a thousand warriors drawn up in battle array.

"Halt!" cried Balboa.

Fearlessly he advanced far ahead of his column, waving his arms in a friendly gesture. A man in the rich dress and ornaments of a cacique came forward to meet him.

"We are here as friends," Balboa greeted him, speaking in the Tule language.

Torecha drew himself up haughtily and replied that if the Spaniards did not turn back there would be a battle.

"No enemy has ever defiled our land," he concluded, "and survived to boast of it."

Balboa said earnestly: "But I speak from my heart, O Torecha, when I tell you we are not enemies. We are friends. We will do you no injury. Our intention is to go straight through your country to the southern sea."

"Not without war," said Torecha angrily and retraced his steps to his warriors.

As compared with Torecha's large force the Spaniards seemed but a handful. Confident of easy victory, the cacique gave the word to attack. Balboa raised his arm and shouted a command to release the war dogs. At the signal his soldiers as well as the dogs rushed forward.

"Ready the guns!" Balboa commanded. "Light fuse. Take aim. Fire!"

A man-made thunderclap broke through the woods, smoke and spitting streaks of flame. Suddenly, there on the ground, Torecha saw many of his fiercest warriors, dead or wounded.

Following up this advantage, for the natives were paralyzed by the awfulness of such magic weapons, Balboa ordered a charge. Except for a halfhearted flight of arrows that fell harmlessly off the armor, shields and steel helmets of his soldiers, there was little resistance. Already the war dogs were tearing mercilessly at the flanks and legs of the retreating natives. Into Torecha's village Balboa followed with his men.

On the 23rd of September Torecha surrendered, glad to make peace on any terms. Much to his astonishment, he was told by Balboa that there would be no reprisals, no prisoners.

"Nor do we even hold bitterness in our hearts against you."

Trinkets were handed out to the cacique and his people and a peace was made. In their turn, the natives brought gifts of food, pearls and gold. Houses were placed at the disposal of the Spanish soldiers. With gladness in his heart, Balboa announced that here, except for a picked group of sixty-seven men and a number of native porters and guides, his company could remain until his return from the South Sea.

"We proceed on our way tomorrow," he said, "if God be willing."

All through the day of September 24th the now greatly diminished band of explorers pushed onward and upward. The trail wound in fairly easy gradients up the side of the mountain. The air grew colder as they ascended.

Camp was made that evening below a cliff that frowned down on them and beside a creek that roared among the rocks. The men huddled around campfires to keep warm, sitting up most of the night speculating about the morrow.

The next day dawned clear. The tips of the underbrush burned red in the rising sun and the creek flashed along with a white flame upon it. Far below, Balboa could hear the waking sounds of the jungle. A huge tapir made his way lazily down a slope. Hawks were circling overhead and the air was moving and pulsing with the rising heat of the lowlands.

An Indian guide threw off his blanket. With stoical face and the slow, graceful walk of the descendant of proud Mayans, he approached Balboa and lifting his arm, pointed.

"He who goes up yonder eminence," he said, "shall look upon the ocean of the south."

Balboa felt a shock, a tearing spasm of emotion. His hands shook.

"Do you speak true?"

"I speak true."

Vasco Núñez bit his unsteady lips. He could not wrench his gaze from that eminence. Any strong man could climb it. But now he felt not strong, but weak. Was it the ravages of fever that made him tremble?

He turned to the company, all of whom had arisen at the news and were also staring upward.

"I go alone," said Balboa quietly.

Not a man spoke. Sword in hand, Balboa turned to the right of the cliff and with sudden eagerness began his climb.

Now and again, stones rattled down. From bush to bush he dragged himself. Then, sheathing his sword, he clambered over a rock wall. Resting there for a moment, he looked back toward his men. With terrible intentness they were watching his every move, their upturned faces like black patches of shadow under their steel helmets.

Balboa went on. The eminence was not easy to climb — not as easy as it had looked. There was no brush now. The rocks were more slippery and the way steeper. A man's breath came short and his hands were cut on sharp edges of shale and stone.

Ten yards more and Balboa had reached the top. He stepped out upon a narrow shoulder, hundreds of feet above the surrounding jungle.

A half gasp, half cry escaped him.

Off upon the rim of the horizon, faintly vignetted between green jungle and haze-filled sky, was something which resembled a wide stretch of water.

Balboa fell to his knees and gave thanks to God. Here, in truth, must be the southern sea. Highway to all the mysterious lands and treasures of the East: El Dorado, the golden temple of Davaive, the famed and fantastic country of Kubla Khan. All here along the border of this great sea. Drama — conquest — discovery — glory for the Spanish realm.

Balboa could not see any more, for his vision blurred and he was wiping moisture from his cheeks. Over and over he kept saying, "Ave Maria. God in all His mercy has given me this day to witness miracles."

CHAPTER XXVIII

PHANTOM OR FULFILLMENT?

ALMOST BEFORE HE WAS AWARE, THE OTHER MEMBERS OF HIS EX-
pedition were crowding around him. They embraced each
other, crying and laughing. Hands shielding their eyes from
the sun's glare they, too, were looking off toward the horizon.

What Comogre's son had told them must be true. A race of
men, down along this coast, who drank from goblets of pure
gold, a people who lived in walled cities interlaced with paved
streets. Temples carved from the solid rock of mountains,
where the vaulted rooms were ornamented with gold, silver
and precious stones. Native gardens where grew all the lush
fruits of the tropics. The smell of spices would be in the air
and the cooling breath of sacred fountains where to bathe
would be to find youth again — and beauty.

And then, suddenly, Balboa gave pause.

From this mountain peak he had looked away to the west.
There he had seen beyond the jungle's verdure what undoubtedly was water. But was it salt water? What proof had he,
after all, that the faintly glimmering streak across the horizon
was the ocean he sought?

Until recently, both he and his followers had accepted as
truth nearly everything the natives had told them: the existence
of certain mountain ranges and cold springs, fabulous monsters
that roved the woods, serpents that were longer than the tallest
trees. On the march a native guide might say, "in a few days
we will come to a village where there is a temple of precious

stones." Seldom did they ever reach such a village or find such a temple. When reprimanded, the guide would find some excuse for himself. "My father," he would say, "told me of this place and he is a very truthful man," or "An evil spirit has caused the jungle to grow around it and over it to conceal it completely."

Time and·again, Balboa had been tricked and deceived. Now his credulity had worn thin. It might have worn out completely had not occasionally the prediction or story of the native come true. In the present case, there was still not enough evidence to prove anything. The expanse of water he had seen might be a large inland lake. It might even be a mirage. After so many disappointments, it would be foolish indeed to raise one's hopes high, only to have them come shattering later about one's ears.

He turned to his followers to see if, by any chance, others were swayed by similar doubts. Perhaps he was too pessimistic. But no. There were a few — one by one, his gaze found them, caught their expressions of disbelief and outright skepticism. Almost to a man, they were of the original expedition that had set sail from Santo Domingo under Enciso. Veterans by now of this wilderness, strong and stern, not easily fooled, not too enthusiastic. Experience had tempered them with caution, and sufferings and discouragements had made them wary. For them there was no ocean until they had something more valid than a view from a hill. They must see it close at hand, mark its ebb and flow, taste its salt.

And here was Pizarro standing apart, his eyes cold and his lips down-curved in a sneer. Walking over to Balboa, he said: "So you believe —?"

"I do not know."

Pizarro stirred some rubble with his foot and then laughed

as he was wont to laugh of late, without humor. It was the kind of laughter from which all the warm glow of living was gone. It chilled Balboa like the ague that comes with fever.

"And what do you think?" Balboa managed to say.

"Another swamp over which the fumes of heat curl in a mist. At this distance the mist resembles water. That is all."

"You think it would be foolhardy then, to go on?"

"I will not say."

Nor would he. Yet that brief conference with Pizarro added still more to Balboa's feeling of defeat. For one glorious moment he had been raised up — he had believed. He had seen victory approaching on winged feet across the awful wastes of wilderness. A few more days — just a few more days struggling through it; possibly a few more lives lost, more hunger, thirst — fever and delirium — and then the goal.

The fabled South Sea! He had been so certain a few minutes ago that he was nearing the end of the road. Ahead had been the promise of paradise — the great East of Marco Polo teeming with its millions of souls, nestling there its culture and civilization. So easy then to visualize the romantic rest-of-the-way, the chance offered to vindicate his name and to prove the worth of his loyalty to his sovereign. Now he was not so sure. Like Pizarro he could not even say. Fumes of heat curling up in a mist above rank swamps or marshlands often did deceive the eye. Often from some hilltop or tall tree he had himself descried what seemed to be water of considerable extent, only to discover later that he had been tricked by the elements.

Pizarro had grown hard of heart, true. But he was also practical. No foolish dreamer, he. The jungle had molded him to her will. Sometimes Balboa wondered if he were not as cunning, as inexorable as it was — aye, and as treacherous.

Sixty-seven members of the party there on the hill and, ex-

cept for the older men, all confident of success. They were
like boys. He had joined their gleeful demonstration a while
ago, but now he stood glum and grim. He knelt when they
knelt to give thanks to God and the Mother Mary. He joined
with them when, led by the priest, Andrés de Vera, they chanted
the *Te Deum ladamus* and *Te Dominum confitemur.*

Then someone said: "We must mark this spot. We must
dedicate this ground to God and our gracious monarch, King
Ferdinand."

Balboa gave them permission to do so, but all the while he
was thinking: "Poor souls, they are happy now — a pity soon
to disillusion them."

Eyes shaded with suffering, he superintended the work of
raising a monument. A tree was felled and a rough cross fash-
ioned from it. Carving the names of the Spanish sovereign
deeply into its wood, they sank its base into a deep hole and
heaped rocks around it. But Pizarro and four or five others
would have no hand in it.

"Fools," Pizarro said, "they are doomed to disappointment.
Wait until they return again this way!"

Balboa heard him, yet went on, dully and deliberately, to ac-
claim to his followers: "I do hereby take possession of this
land and all lands laved by the southern sea in the name of our
most puissant lords, the sovereigns of Castile."

The words choked him. A document was then drawn up
by the notary, Andrés de Valderrábano, at Balboa's request.
All present were asked to inscribe their names upon it as witnesses. Pizarro, the last called upon to sign, stepped back angrily and shook his head.

"I shall subscribe to no such nonsense," he said. "Not until,
if ever, we come to the shores of this improbable sea. To my
mind, the whole thing lacks verification."

Balboa thought so too, but this was neither the time nor the place to state such an opinion. Its effect upon the expedition would be disastrous. Mirage, swamp mists, or whatever it might later prove to be, the illusion of the sea was there and it had inspired the majority of his followers. To cast doubt now would be to blank forever all possibility of success. More than that, it would lead to death itself, for no man with defeat in his heart and fever in his bones could survive the way back. There had to be hope to nourish strength to feed the languishing blood stream. Confidence that they were nearing the end of their journey, the fulfillment of their hopes, was the only thing that could save them. Was Francisco Pizarro not aware of this? By his stubbornness would he imperil the lives of them all?

Filled with apprehension, Balboa saw that already questioning looks were being exchanged among those who had heard what Pizarro said. A crisis was near. Sensing it, Balboa acted quickly.

Springing toward his second-in-command, he caught his arm and half pulled, half escorted the rebellious soldier beyond the hearing of his men.

"Now," he said, "we may be of the same mind, but not of the same heart. Do you wish every man of us to be destroyed?"

"No." Pizarro scowled.

"Then hold your tongue!"

For a moment, white-hot anger made livid the cheeks of Pizarro. Defiance gleamed in his dark eyes. One hand fluttered to his halberd, then dropped. He could see lightning flints striking sparks in the gaze of the man he knew to be his master.

"Aye, sir."

Balboa thrust the document toward him. "Sign it."

Without an instant's hesitation, Pizarro signed.

Shouldering their equipment once more, the little company marched in single file down the western slope of the mountain. The Province of Chiapes, another difficult region, lay ahead. According to the native guides the province was no more than two miles in breadth, less than an hour's walk under ordinary conditions. But under the conditions imposed by the jungle, Balboa could see that his party must chop every foot of the way. Never had he looked upon such a mass of creeping vines, snarled undergrowth and thick-set trees, rank upon rank, crowding back to the place where, from the mountain, they had seen what resembled water.

They were not, any of them, physically fit for the gigantic job that faced them, even though willing to undertake it. Balboa glanced down at his own blistered and bleeding hands. For hours on end they must hack away with axe and sword. They must tug and pull and strain and flounder, ankle-deep in water, prey to the bites of insects, leeches and snakes. Scarcely a man who had not, some time or other, suffered from the fever. Many were still so afflicted. Hardships had worn deep lines in their faces. Hunger had made them thin and weak. Their bodies were masses of sores from infected bites and poisonous thorns.

Yet not one, even the rebellious Pizarro, who would not willingly follow him to the death. That realization so touched Balboa that, standing there, before this new barrier, his eyes grew wet. Where could be found a more courageous and loyal crew, though he searched the world for them?

"On!" he cried, and sprang forward, axe in hand. "I will match strokes with you. On to the goal!"

Blades of steel made the woods echo. Now and again came the crashing descent of some tall tree, whipping loose from its viny tangle, cracking off branches of its neighbors until, at last, it thundered to the ground.

Balboa's men now worked as never before. Hope they had — a sort of childish unreasoning hope perhaps — but it was accomplishing miracles. Steadily they tunneled through the forest. A green curtain that shut out the sky. A jungle twilight that knew no sun even when it blazed high at noon. Monkeys screaming in retreat before them and jaguars darting for new cover. Short pauses for drink and food. Ministering aids for axemen injured by falling branches. Soldiers rescued from grass-covered bogholes without bottom. Vine bridges across streams too deep or too swift to ford. Battles with anacondas and encounters, now and again, with Indians lying in ambush with poisoned darts.

Two days of contesting every inch of the way. Then, so suddenly that it seemed unbelievable, a broken wall of trees emerged upon a sand beach!

Ahead of them for a mile, in a blaze of sun they had not seen for long hours — sand. No plant or bush, no creepers, no stagnant pools. Sand! Sand spread out white and clean in shocking contrast to the green that had smothered them. White, white sand!

Their eyes, accustomed to the shadow made by encircling trees and covering vines, could not at first withstand the glare. The air was clear as glass. It was as if they had come to a new world of ineffable brightness. Beyond, to the horizon, not a single barrier, but a great endless space unoccupied by mountain, morass or jungle.

For a long moment, no one moved or spoke. Each was trying to read from the eyes of his fellows what this might portend. What was it? An ancient lake bottom, the edge of a salt marsh? Disappointment showed on every face. Balboa could hear the man next to him gulping. As in a dream he saw Pizarro hurl his halberd to the ground and call upon the gods to witness their undoing.

"A million curses upon this accursed land!" he cried, and sat down, head pillowed in his arms.

There was another long silence. All of the members of Balboa's expedition were either sitting or lying just where they had come out from the jungle. They had neither heart nor strength left. Bearded faces stared into bearded faces. Unkempt hair fell upon ragged shoulders. Eyes, puffed from insect bites, closed in utter weariness and despair.

How long they remained thus, broken and defeated, Balboa never knew. His mind was whirling in an effort to think straight, to raise up his courage to the point where he could offer them some shred of hope.

Once he cleared his throat, tried to speak, but the words choked him. He started to rise, then sat down again. There was nothing to say — after all, there was nothing to say. A chimera of wide ocean and its bordering lands of gold had faded and bleached into sand. The edge of some inland desert, no doubt. Comogre's son had lied to them. Perhaps some of the fury of Pizarro had found lodgment in Balboa's own chest. His breathing quickened. His eyes fired. He kept clenching and unclenching his hands.

A shout from one of the men brought him quickly alert. The soldier, a little dark-eyed man from Castile, pointed excitedly. A short distance to their right were two native canoes, dry beached, but apparently in perfect condition.

"Why should they leave them here?" Balboa wondered. "So far from water."

Hurriedly he dispatched a scouting party with instructions to search for an Indian village. Also to learn, if possible, if there was not a river or lake near by. If there were canoes, there must be water. By the same token, if there were canoes, there must be Indians. It was about all they could hope for now — food and rest against the day they must turn back toward Darien in ignominy and defeat.

One hour — two hours — wore on. Sitting, head slightly forward, arms around his knees, Balboa continued to gaze southward. The belt of sand held a strange fascination for him. Just as there were patterns of shade, so here there were patterns of light, or degrees of light, shimmering and gleaming out there. In places, the light seemed to move as it sometimes moves along wave-crests or ripples in the water. It was growing brighter. It was moving faster. Flashes as of sun on glass. A glint here, sparkle there — and strange! — that deadly whiteness was disappearing. Simultaneously to his ears came a faint roar.

Balboa leapt to his feet, and raced across the sand to meet it.

Glory to God, it was the tide coming in!

Rolling and tumbling along the unspotted beach — the salt tide! He tasted it. He quaffed it, laughing. Water flooded around his knees, rolled up to his thighs. From his scabbard he flung out his sword, raising it high.

Others were splashing behind him. The two canoes were being launched and Alonso Martín, a foot soldier from Seville, clambered into one of them and shouted: "Friends, be ye witness that I am the first Spaniard ever to be upon the waters of this sea in a boat!"

Such a din they made! The roar of the tide and the men's shouting and shrieking like children gone wild with joy.

Of them all, Balboa alone was quiet. A great peace had fallen over him. Wading back to shore, he looked out, far out, into the dimming distance. There were blue sky and white clouds, edged with the red of a lowering sun. Below them, not mist, but the smoke-haze that rises ever upon great ocean expanses held his attention.

Here was the South Sea.

He had found it at last. Here was attainment. Here was the white shining trail to new adventure.

CHAPTER XXIX

EXPLORATION AND RETURN

VOICES FROM THE WOODS PRESENTLY ANNOUNCED THE RETURN OF the scouting party. Immediately Balboa selected twenty-five men and set out to follow the shore line of the inlet to the main ocean beach. The sight that met his eyes he knew he could never forget. Here, in truth, was what he had come to find. In all of its majesty and might, vast and unaccountable, the sea that lay at his feet was worthy to be compared to the Atlantic — aye, that might even prove to be a larger one. The tide was thundering in. Seizing his sword and flourishing it aloft, holding his shield and the royal banner on which the picture of the Virgin was painted on one side, and, upon the other, the royal coat of arms, Balboa waded out, waist deep, and stood still amid the swirling waters. In a loud and resonant voice he proclaimed:

"Long live the high and powerful monarchs, Don Ferdinand and Doña Juana, sovereigns of Castile and of Leon and Aragon, in whose name and for the royal crown of Castile, I take and seize real and corporeal actual possession of these seas and lands, and of the coasts and ports and islands of the south, with all thereto annexed, together with the kingdoms and provinces which belong to them, or which may hereafter belong to them, in whatever name and by whatever right and title acquired, now existing or which may exist, ancient or modern, in times past and present and to come, without any contradiction whatsoever.

"And if any other prince or captain, Christian or infidel, of whatever law or sect or condition he may be, presumes any right to these lands and sea, I am ready and prepared to contradict him and to defend them in the names of the present and future sovereigns of Castile, who are the lords paramount in these Indies, islands and Terra Firma, northern or southern, with their seas, as well in the arctic pole as in the antarctic, on either side of the equinoctial line, within or without the tropics of Cancer and Capricorn, according to what more completely to their majesties and their successors belongs and is due, for the whole and any part thereof, as I protest in writing shall or may be more fully specified and alleged on behalf of their royal patrimony, now and in all time while the earth revolves, and until the universal judgment of all mankind."

Except for a few changes here and there, it was the same declaration of discovery and intention Admiral Columbus had made upon that memorable day when he had first set foot in the New World. And it was the same speech Rodrigo de Bastidas and other explorers had repeated after him; for, although it might be grandiloquent and somewhat bombastic, it still was the official language of discovery. Balboa had committed it to memory years before. Though its phraseology was rather confusing to a man of simplicity, he knew that it sounded impressive, as impressive as the occasion itself.

His followers cheered as he concluded solemnly and struggled back to shore. Water sprayed his face and he could taste its salt. This was indeed no great fresh-water lake as some had suspected, but an ocean of unknown expanse. He asked the others to taste of it. They nodded their heads sagely and declared it to be a true salt sea. They had reached their goal at last.

Balboa named the bay which he had just discovered El Golfo

de San Miguel in commemoration of St. Michael, as this was St. Michael's Day, September 29th. Proceeding at once to the Chiapes village, he distributed gifts and made protestations of peace and friendship. Guides and porters were enlisted.

For a full month Balboa and his handful of men journeyed up and down the coast, marking trees with the royal insignia, questioning the natives and drawing rough maps of the region for future use.

One day they were presented to the cacique, Tumaco, whose village lay ideally situated a few leagues north of El Golfo de San Miguel. As a token of his regard, Tumaco gave Balboa a sizable gourd which, when he shook it, rattled curiously. Prying off the cover, Balboa was amazed to behold its contents. Three hundred or more lovely pearls!

Where had Tumaco secured them?

Smiling, the cacique pointed toward an island just opposite the village. Pearl fishing, he said, was pursued with great success by the islanders living there and on nearby islands.

Balboa named the largest of these islands Isla Rica, but later the entire group came to be known as the Pearl Islands.

Through an interpreter, Tumaco asked the Spaniards many questions. Whence had they come? What were their plans for the future? By what magic did they make the lightning and thunder that came from those curious iron sticks?

Balboa answered patiently and, in turn, sought information of a wealthy land lying somewhere along these coasts. A land of gold and emeralds, it was said. Had Tumaco heard of it?

"Aye," said the interpreter, after listening attentively to the chief.

"How far?"

"Until the sun has journeyed forth and back a score of times or more."

"Who are the people living in this fabulous land?"

"The Incas."

It was the second time Vasco Núñez had heard that name and it confirmed his highest hopes. The Orient it must be, for Tumaco had spoken of queer four-legged beasts of burden which he called llamas. These undoubtedly were the camels of the caravan routes of the East. Slowly but surely he was tracing down the truth, drawing nearer to Cathay. He could hardly wait until he could return to Darien and make preparations for another expedition.

Loaded down with gold and pearls, Balboa set out upon the return trip on November 3, 1513. In order to make quicker progress and learn more of the country, he chose a different route going back. It was as difficult as the first, however, and many of the men suffered from malaria. Balboa himself was forced to allow himself to be carried part of the way back on a hammock borne by two native porters. On January 5, 1514, Balboa arrived with his heroic band at Ponca's village.

Here he received information, the first in long months, of Darien and its progress in his absence. Two ships had arrived there recently, it was said, from Española. Balboa was overjoyed and quickly began to recover his health and spirits. Once more leading his men, he reached Careta's village on January 17th. Accompanied by a picked crew of twenty men, Balboa proceeded to Aclá, took ship and arrived in Santa María, Darien, on January 19th.

Somehow, news of his exploits had preceded him. He disembarked to the salute of cannon and an ovation that re-echoed to the jungle's depths.

Among the first to greet him was Don Pedro de Arbolancha, Ferdinand's special envoy, who had but recently arrived in Darien. Arbolancha's mission was a secret one. He had come

to investigate conditions and the character and standing of
Vasco Núñez de Balboa himself. It was not long before his
growing admiration of the great discoverer made him confide
in him. His findings, he told Balboa, were very favorable to
him.

"Indeed," he said, "I am convinced by the facts so apparent
and by your accomplishments so evident, that there is nothing
which your enemies can prove against you." He extended his
hand. "I would be proud if you would consider me your
friend."

Balboa was deeply warmed by that kindly tribute and by the
affectionate loyalty of the settlers at Darien. Later, when Arbolancha was preparing to return to make his report, Vasco
Núñez gave him a letter for King Ferdinand in which he described in detail his journey across the isthmus and the discovery of the new sea.

Soon after, Arbolancha set sail. Two months had passed in
reconditioning his vessel, stocking it with food, and taking
aboard gold and pearls, Balboa's gift to his monarch.

Now, at last, thought Vasco Núñez de Balboa, he had truly
acquitted himself. He was firmly entrenched in his position
as leader of the Darien colony and discoverer of the southern
ocean. Not in vain had he come all this way, enduring and
suffering and praying — watching over his men by night and
day, rising to each fresh emergency that his little band might
not be wiped out.

CHAPTER XXX

DON PEDRARIAS ARRIVES

Dawn had scarcely begun to invade the tropic darkness when Balboa awoke. For some reason which he could not fathom he had spent a restless night, twisting, turning, falling into shallow slumber crowded with distorted nightmare faces, then jerking back to consciousness to stare wide-eyed into the dimness of his room.

It was June 29, 1514. Not an important date, he thought, except that it was the day he had arranged to start the rethatching of the roof of his dwelling. He rose, blinking the sleep from his eyes and trying, as he did so, to rout the strange depression from his mind.

He went to the cabin doorway and stretched, moving his great shoulders and feeling the pleasant easy pull of muscles beneath his skin.

Looking out over the settlement, he smiled slowly, his spirits lifting. Never had the Darien colony been more prosperous. The two hundred palm-thatched cabins, the municipal buildings and the one church stood sturdily on the level bank of the river. Five hundred and fifteen Spaniards and fifteen hundred Indians, both freemen and slaves, dwelt together here in harmony.

He could see beyond the settlement the neat, well-kept gardens and young thriving orchards. Since his return from the expedition to the South Sea, Balboa had urged that the colonists devote their efforts mainly to village improvements and crop cultivation. Everything was flourishing. Balboa looked forward to an abundant harvest. It was his hope that eventually the colony might be able to grow enough provisions to be self-sufficient. Now, however, it was enough to know peace and comparative security. Because of the friendship pacts Balboa had made with more than twenty caciques, no Spaniard venturing into the surrounding jungle need fear hostile attack. They were safe wherever they went.

Indeed, thought the settlement's commander, watching the rising sun thin the veiling mists that drifted lazily among the quiet cottages, existence here had become as simple as in civilized Spain. On festival days they had their games and tilting matches; on other days they labored in town or in the fields, or went on hunting expeditions; on the Sabbath they attended holy services conducted by the Franciscan friars.

He could not help the pride which stirred within him, knowing that this contentment was largely due to his own able leadership. Surely when King Ferdinand should hear the favorable report of Pedro de Arbolancha, he would be won to favor. By this time, Pedro must be nearly arrived in Seville.

Two hours later he was busy helping the Indian workers with the roof thatching. He worked as one of them, not harshly commanding, but cheerfully suggesting. The sun beat full upon him, so that even the loose cotton shirt and drawers and the light hempen sandals felt somewhat too warm. He sighed and wished it might be considered proper for the ruler of Darien to wear as little as the Indians.

He called, and the little maid Fulvia came hurrying with a cooling drink.

He lifted the vessel, but stopped, for over its rim he saw a young Spanish cavalier approaching, attired with all the elegant splendor of old Seville. It was long since any man in Darien had seen such attire, and Balboa's eyes widened in astonishment.

The other, too, seemed taken aback at Balboa's appearance, for he stammered dubiously:

"Vasco Núñez de Balboa?"

"Aye."

"I come from Don Pedrarias Dávila, newly appointed Governor of Darien. His fleet has anchored in the bay about a league and a half away."

Balboa's body felt numb, but his thoughts were in chaotic action. A new governor! He was, then, to be displaced — the labors, perils, sufferings and achievements of four years had gone for naught. His letters to his king, his steadfast loyalty, his discovery of the great South Sea and his untiring efforts to increase the Spanish domain — these all had come to this one result: another was to be nourished on his fruits.

Still, he reminded himself more temperately, no doubt his king was doing what he believed best for the colony. His opinion of Balboa had been poisoned by the lying and envious Enciso, had been influenced by the seeming, rather than the actual. The new governor must have been appointed before the court had received Arbolancha's news of the discovery of the South Sea, and have left Spain before Arbolancha arrived. Therefore, he could not in justice blame either King Ferdinand or this new governor, Don Pedrarias Dávila. His own authority had somehow bred in him a respect for that of others.

He lifted his head. "Tell Don Pedrarias that he is welcome. We of Darien are at his service."

The followers of Balboa were filled with indignation, however. Why should another be elevated to the place won with such effort by Balboa? Could experience at the Spanish court

fit a man for leadership in this rigorous wilderness? Those
who had struggled loyally by Balboa's side fighting Indian
battles, toiling in the fields for food to sustain a scant existence, floundering through treacherous swamps, hewing a path
through the green matted jungle, and finally climbing ardu-
ously to that Darien peak to behold the South Sea — these men
righteously rebelled.

"We'll not permit the landing of this man!" they shouted.
"Have we not earned through hardship the right to choose our
ruler?"

Balboa's face was grim. "What you suggest is mutiny
against the king and Spain. Already we have gained a lawless
reputation. Would you make it worse? Would you have our
enemies wag their heads in triumph and say: 'Did we not tell
of the wicked impudence of those at Darien? Behold, it is
proven!'"

Reluctantly they agreed to the wisdom of their leader's arguments, but with faces nearly as long as when awaiting the
arrival of the unfortunate Diego de Nicuesa.

"Be cheerful," urged Balboa, "when the new governor comes.
Pedrarias must find naught lacking in our welcome."

Therefore, the colonists went forth unarmed the next day
to meet the new governor and his brilliant company.

Not so trustful was Pedrarias. Two thousand men formed
his bodyguard, resplendent in shining armor and brocade, their
shields dazzling in the sun. Don Pedro Arias Dávila was accompanied by his wife, Doña Isabella, and the new Bishop of
Darien, Fray Juan de Quevedo, in his impressive robes of
office.

Balboa strode forward, his great frame and proud fiery head
overshadowing the shabbiness of his attire. All eyes were upon

him, critically appraising. Balboa greeted the new governor with respectful dignity, promising the allegiance of himself and his men.

More than sixty years old was Don Pedrarias, and his shrewd eyes, neither brown nor blue but a peculiar mixture of both, looked narrowly at Vasco Núñez de Balboa. Balboa's clear gaze met his steadily, studying this man whom the king had chosen to favor in his stead.

Don Pedrarias' skin was dark and coarse-grained, deeply furrowed. Grizzled hair framed his countenance like a grotesque halo and his lips were two tight uncompromising lines. His appearance was far from encouraging. The face of his wife, however, was filled with a patient uncomplaining wisdom, and the greeting she gave to Balboa was kindly. In the eyes of Fray Juan de Quevedo, as well, Balboa found a kind of compassionate admiration.

Searching the other personages, Balboa's heart lurched sickeningly. It couldn't be — yet it was — Enciso! The lawyer stood near Pedrarias, apparently a counselor, and there was malicious triumph in his little gleaming eyes.

He has come back to gloat, Balboa thought, and knew that the fabric of the colony's peace, woven so painstakingly, was rent now beyond repair. His first thought was for the colony, not for himself.

What Balboa felt, however, he was resolved not to show. He escorted the new arrivals back to the town. His battered veterans mingled with the fashionably dressed cavaliers from Spain.

A banquet was given for the guests, but the roots, maize, and casaba bread were looked upon as novelties and supplies were brought from the ships to supplement them.

Throughout, Pedrarias maintained his attitude of reserved

tolerance toward Balboa. Only when he learned of the recent discovery of the South Sea did the mask slip momentarily from him. Resentment, burning for a brief unguarded instant from his eyes, seemed to glow from the very wrinkles of his shrunken face. But the others, his wife, Doña Isabella and Fray Juan de Quevedo, received the news with swift admiration. After a brief disappointment in not having a part in the heroic achievement, the cavaliers listened with growing excitement to the story, dreaming of golden realms and untold riches.

Every courtesy was shown to Pedrarias' company. The most spacious dwellings were given them and slaves to wait upon them. Gifts were presented, the colonists dividing their own treasure generously.

Balboa himself brought some of his finest pearls to the Doña Isabella. The smile of thanks she gave him somehow choked his throat, for her eyes made him remember his own mother.

If only the man whom Isabella de Bobadilla, niece of the noted Marquésa de Moya, had married had resembled her in disposition and character!

The following day Vasco Núñez de Balboa was summoned to a private interview with Pedrarias. Only one other was present, the chief notary, Oviedo, who recorded the meeting.

Pedrarias' greeting was cordial. He told Balboa that His Majesty, King Ferdinand, was very favorably impressed with his work, as was Pedrarias himself. He had been instructed, he said, to seek Balboa's very excellent advice regarding the colonial affairs.

Balboa, ever trusting, quickly felt ashamed of his previous suspicion of this friendly old courtier. He told himself that the unfavorable circumstances of their meeting must have unduly prejudiced his mind. Here was no highhanded fox, eager to hasten his downfall, but a man humble enough to seek the opinions of someone younger and of lower birth than himself and whom a lesser character might well consider inferior.

"Your experience in this land is exceedingly valuable," said Pedrarias smoothly. "If you would be kind enough to pass your knowledge concerning the surrounding country on to me, I will greatly profit thereby in administering the affairs of this colony."

Eager to please, Balboa offered to submit a complete written report to the Governor.

"I will have it for you in two days," he promised.

Leaving Pedrarias' presence, Balboa felt comforted. True, he had lost all rank in the colony he had built and was now but a common soldier, but at least Zamudio's worst fears were not being realized. He had not been arrested, as the Biscayan soldier had warned. He was free. Pedrarias had asked his aid. In time, he might climb back to a position where he might be of benefit to the settlement again, and to King Ferdinand and Spain.

He worked long and earnestly on the report. Luaia, bewildered by the swift course of events, came at intervals to place food before him.

"Vas-co," she said anxiously, "you are sure these new men do not bring trouble for you?"

He patted her absently. "Aye. Do not worry."

"But why are you not still the ruler of Darien?"

He tried to explain, but since his own mind dwelt in confusion, he could not make it clear to her. She listened, downcast, as he fumbled for words.

"Is it your king who is not willing that you rule — or your great Christian God?" she faltered in bewilderment.

Balboa sat staring beyond her. "I do not know," he said. "I do not know." Then he smiled and drew her close. "But things could be worse. We are both safe — and together. Is not that enough?"

"Aye," agreed Luaia, her dark eyes shining. "If it is enough for you, then it is for me."

"And nothing can ever change the fact," continued Balboa, a glorious remembering in his tired eyes, "that it was I who first caught sight of the great South Sea and laid claim to all its golden lands in the name of King Ferdinand and Spain."

Through the nightmare days that followed, it was a thought he clung to. For scarcely had his painstakingly detailed report been placed in Pedrarias' eager hands than Vasco Núñez de Balboa and his former officers were arrested. A residencia, or official inquiry into the explorer's acts during his term of jurisdiction over the province of Darien, was ordered.

CHAPTER XXXI

INJUSTICE AND CALAMITY

THE YOUNG LICENTIATE, GASPAR DE ESPINOSA, WHO HAD COME with Pedrarias to be alcalde mayor of the colony, was appointed to prosecute Balboa. So recently had he left the University of Salamanca that this was his first case. He was easily swayed by others, anxious to be agreeable to those in power and, of course, to prove his merits by winning his initial legal battle.

Naturally, Enciso was eager to aid Espinosa against the man toward whom he felt such ceaseless enmity. Fray Juan de Quevedo, however, convinced of Balboa's worth since their first meeting, used his influence in Balboa's behalf. He discovered that Pedrarias was conducting a secret investigation by interviewing followers of Ojeda and Nicuesa. It was plain that the new governor was intent on ruining Balboa by convicting him of usurping and abusing power.

The bishop, therefore, denounced Pedrarias' unfair methods to young Espinosa, saying that a secret inquiry was a reflection on the ability of the alcalde. Thus aroused, Espinosa went to Pedrarias and complained, insisting that he be allowed to conduct the matter in his own way.

As a result Balboa, although acquitted of the alleged crimes, was found guilty of seizing Enciso's property. A judgment was awarded his enemy. In addition, other suits were brought against him until he was hopelessly tangled in litigation and finally left penniless.

Pedrarias now announced that he intended to send Balboa back to Spain in chains.

Balboa, forlorn and utterly discouraged, received this news almost indifferently. He had borne so much injustice that additional persecution could not matter. Grimly, he remembered that the great admiral, Christopher Columbus, had been thus dealt with by the envious Bobadilla. At least he shared the fate of the great, he thought. It was bitter comfort.

Luaia, however, was desolate. Although they were living now in the smallest, meanest cabin in the settlement, she had striven to bring him what solace she could through her loyalty and devotion. But now if her lord were to be taken from her — how could she bear it? The grief of separation, the fear for his safety, the terrible resentment against his harassers — these choked her.

"Ai-ee! They will take you from me! I cannot endure the pain!"

Balboa looked at her broodingly. "I have brought you only trouble."

"It is not so! You brought me only love, Vas-co. It is those others — they have brought the trouble. How can it be? How dare they do such things to you — you so strong and good?"

He took her small oval face in his two hands, turning it up to his.

"I want you to make me a promise," he said.

She nodded.

"If I should leave you, in whatever manner, you must not remain here. I want you to return to your father, Careta. You will be safer there."

Her soft chin trembled. "But I do not want to leave you!"

"Nor I," he sighed. "Yet there comes a time when even the

strongest man cannot choose. Promise, Luaia. It will lighten the heaviness of my heart."

The words came shakenly. "I promise."

But the time of their separation was not yet. Quevedo intervened again. He persuaded Pedrarias that it would be folly to send the discoverer of the South Sea back to Spain, that his deeds had by now probably made him a hero, that the king would receive him with favor and reward him with power instead of punishment.

"He will doubtless return," argued the bishop, "with greater rank and power than ever before."

So Pedrarias, encouraged in this by his wife who also sympathized with Balboa, relented. He gave Balboa a reprieve, but restricted his activity to that of a paroled prisoner whose conduct needed close watching.

Thus Balboa lost his one chance of securing justice at the Spanish court. Quevedo, who had meant to aid him, had really done him harm in the long run, and in the months to come Balboa often regretted that Pedrarias had stayed his hand. Real chains could not have harmed his spirit nor reputation more than the subtle ceaseless insinuations of Pedrarias.

Though treating Balboa with such gross cruelty, Pedrarias by no means scorned his previous advice, but turned it instead to his own advantage. Balboa, in his written report, had suggested that a line of posts be established at intervals between Darien and the South Sea. Pedrarias at once set out to do this, but calamity, unimpressed by the arrival of highborn, adventurous cavaliers from Seville, once more flattened the settlement.

The building erected for the storing of supplies brought from Spain was destroyed by fire. It was whispered by some, and very cautiously, that this had been ordered by Pedrarias himself to cover his taking most of the food for himself and his officers. No one dared press the charge, but certainly it was evident that none of the governor's men experienced want as did others.

Close upon the first disaster came a second. Grasshoppers swarmed down upon the fields, destroying most of the crops. The highhearted young gallants from Spain were the first to suffer from the dreadful famine. Many, too, weakened by hunger, died from fever. Sickness and starvation were everywhere. Those who had looked down their noses in disdain at the native food at first, were now begging to exchange their elegant embroidered silks for a handful of maize or some casaba bread. Finally, they did not scorn grass, bark and roots as food.

Pedrarias himself became ill. Taking with him generous supplies, he departed for the nearby mountainous country where the climate was supposed to be more healthful. Before he left with his physician, he gave permission for all who so desired to leave Darien. An entire shipload gladly abandoned the settlement, setting out for Cuba and Spain. Pedrarias himself declared that, when he was well enough, he meant to return to Seville, but his council refused to let him go. Grumbling, the governor remained and in after years tried to take credit to himself for his loyalty in remaining with the settlement.

In all, seven hundred perished either from fever or starvation. All might have died had not two ships with provisions arrived opportunely. Pedrarias decided to reduce the number of hungry mouths by sending out expeditions to form settlements at the posts suggested by Balboa. Balboa himself was the obvious one to send, for he knew both the countryside and the natives, but Pedrarias ignored his qualifications.

Captain Juan de Ayora was sent instead with four hundred men, in one large ship and four caravels. Balboa was apprehensive.

"I like not this Juan de Ayora," he told Hernando de Argüello privately. "There is ruthlessness in the set of his mouth and greed in his eyes. I fear he will not consider the friendship I have made between the caciques and ourselves."

Argüello shook his head glumly. "I 'm afraid you are right. Such is his reputation."

When, after several months, Ayora had not been heard from, another expedition was organized to look for him. Quevedo managed to have Bartolomé Hurtado selected for this command.

In February, 1515, Hurtado returned to the settlement. With him were a hundred slaves, all obviously ill-treated. He had secured two thousand pesos of gold, as well. Ayora, he reported, was safe. Many of his men, however, reported that both Ayora and Hurtado had plundered and harassed the entire country, treating friendly Indian tribes as mercilessly as those who resisted. The formerly hospitable caciques were either slain or had become hostile.

Balboa was horrified to find that Hurtado had made slaves of the Indians the cacique, Careta, had loaned him as porters.

Luaia wailed in his arms. "Ai-ee! What disaster has befallen my father's people! The villages ravaged, the lands plundered, the friends and relatives of my childhood slain and enslaved. Who knows what befell my father and my brothers?"

Balboa choked, his own heart equally torn: "I heard — I heard they fled and escaped."

A greater rage than he had ever known assailed him. The fury in him was like a lump, growing, growing, so that it seemed he must give vent to it or be broken by its force. Into his mind came the pictures of scenes he remembered: peaceful native villages, curtained thick with jungle or spread out on some wide fertile plateau; a bent native woman, her black hair shining sleekly in the sun, busily grinding maize; a stalwart cacique, presenting gifts with childlike simplicity; naked brown children, black-eyed and easily alarmed by the imposing strangers; Careta, Luaia's father, coming forth to greet the Spaniards, his face calm, his manner dignified; Comogre's son, christened Carlos, courageously striking the scales, his eyes scornful. Rightly scornful, Balboa thought now. Perhaps Carlos had known the atrocities of which nominal Christians were capable. Carlos, they said, had fled after Ayora's treacherous attack to a neighboring country where he had been slain.

Something must be done, decided Balboa, his clenched fists aching. Then, feeling his own impotence, he put his head in his hands. The fury rising in him receded suddenly. Bleak emptiness took its place, harder to bear than anger.

There was nothing he could do — nothing anyone could do. This was a land where gold begot greed, and greed, blood — and blood a relentless reign of terror. He had striven in vain for a more temperate conquest. He was defeated.

When Luis Botello came with the news that Hurtado had ingratiated himself with Pedrarias and his officials by presenting them with slaves, he received the information with weary resignation.

Eight months later, Ayora returned. He had left the majority of his force at two settlements, and had returned with slaves and plunder. He, too, distributed slaves among the men in power. Then, pleading that his health had been greatly impaired by his campaigns, he returned to Spain. It was suspected that he took with him a great quantity of stolen gold which he neither reported nor paid the legal fifth to the king.

Pedrarias, it was said, condoned his departure because of his friendship with Ayora's brother.

On March 20th, 1515, a ship arrived from Spain with dispatches from King Ferdinand. Since it was the first word received from the king after learning of Balboa's discovery of the South Sea, Balboa mingled eagerly with the seamen to find out how he was regarded.

"There is a letter for you from the king," one told him. "It is said to confer upon you high honors, as indeed all Spain regards you as a hero, second only to Columbus."

"Then," stammered Balboa eagerly, "King Ferdinand regards me favorably?"

"Aye, very. It is rumored that he has commissioned you governor of the new lands you have discovered and captain of the South Sea. But you will read for yourself when the letter is delivered to you by Pedrarias."

But Pedrarias withheld the letter. Days went by, and still no dispatches were given into Balboa's keenly desirous hands. It became apparent that Pedrarias was determined that he should not have the honors.

Incensed at this, Balboa appealed to the bishop, his only friend among the governor's counselors. Meanwhile, Quevedo himself, knowing of the appointment, had been enraged by Pedrarias' unlawful actions. Failing to persuade the governor to give over the letters, he preached a sermon in church on the subject. Alarmed, Pedrarias, after consulting Espinosa, called a meeting of his council to decide on the matter. Quevedo's was the only dissenting voice in the decision that Balboa should not be awarded his honors until after the king had received a report on his residencia.

"But the residencia has lasted nine months, when it should have been terminated in sixty days, according to the king's own instructions," protested Quevedo hotly. He continued, declaring their disregard of the king's wishes was nothing less than pure treason. How dared they question the king's commands?

"It is plain that envy, rather than justice, moves you," he cried. "If you do this thing, you yourselves will have to answer for it to His Majesty." He painted a vivid picture of the king's probable reactions.

Thus violently faced with the truth, Pedrarias reconsidered. He was not bothered by conscience, long since atrophied, but by fear that blame might fall on him. He rose shakily to his feet and addressed his cowed council.

"It is my opinion that Vasco Núñez de Balboa be given his commission tomorrow."

So, one long month after the dispatches reached the hands of the jealous Pedrarias, Balboa received his honors. He read them off to Luaia, boyish with excitement. Indeed, it was only the second time in the history of Spain that the title of adelantado had been awarded, he explained to her.

She listened breathlessly and with proud, brimming eyes as he recited: "Adelantado. Captain of the South Sea and Governor of Terra Nueva, Panama and Coiba." He seized her and danced her gaily around the little cabin. "It means that I have been raised to high nobility and that my realms are greater than those of Pedrarias himself!"

But Balboa's joy was short-lived. The king, in all good faith, had attached a condition to these titles and honors that made them of little actual worth.

Although instructed to explore and settle Terra Nueva, Balboa was commanded to secure Pedrarias' approval of any undertaking and to be subject to his directions. King Ferdinand, decided Balboa in disappointment, had apparently not known of Pedrarias' true character, or he would not thus have hampered the man he wished to honor.

He learned, too, that Pedrarias was writing a letter to the king defaming him, and even declaring that Nicuesa instead of Balboa had really discovered the South Sea!

The plundering and slaying of the natives of Terra Firma went on. Ayora not having been punished for his terrible actions, other captains followed his example, until there was not an Indian who did not fear and hate the conquering Spaniards. In reprisal, they fell upon the soldiers at every opportunity, wiping out settlements, which Pedrarias sent men to establish, and making the countryside unsafe for any except large, well-armed forces of Spaniards.

In ten months, five of Pedrarias' expeditions had failed. Knowing Balboa's former success, the Governor of Darien grew nearly insane with jealousy of the younger man.

In an attempt to obscure Balboa's achievements, he sent another to explore and rename lands already visited by the adelantado. Gaspar de Morales, a cousin of Pedrarias, was chosen and he visited more horror upon the lands than even the heartless Ayora. Hearing of his exploits, Balboa felt compelled to write a protest to the king, who was never in favor of such inhumanity.

Others shared Balboa's righteous indignation. Among them was Oviedo, chief notary and inspector of the royal mines. He disapproved heartily of all the bloodshed and injustice rampant under Pedrarias. He decided to return to Spain and at the same time Quevedo sent one of his loyal friars as well.

Knowing that these men would report Balboa's treatment to the Spanish court, the wily Pedrarias announced just before their departure that Balboa was to lead an expedition.

CHAPTER XXXII

FURTHER TREACHERY

BALBOA HOPED THAT THE EXPEDITION HE WAS TO LEAD WOULD be to the shores of the South Sea, but this was not according to Pedrarias' well laid plans. He sent Balboa to find the Golden Temple of Davaive which previously he had sought in vain. Then, the dangers from natives and nature had been great; now, they were greater, for the Spaniards had spread ruin in Terra Firma and the Indians sought revenge.

Not only did Pedrarias send Balboa to almost certain failure, but he protected his own interests in case some miracle crowned the adelantado with success. Luis Carillo, one of Pedrarias' favorite officers, was selected to share the command, so that if the enterprise succeeded he, rather than Balboa, might receive the credit.

Neither was Balboa's residencia ended. He was merely given temporary release, approved by all except the unforgiving Enciso.

Being provided with insufficient equipment, ambushed and attacked by the natives, the expedition lived up to Pedrarias' malicious expectations and Balboa returned to Darien a failure, his prestige dimmed.

Of all those in authority in the settlement, Quevedo alone still supported Balboa publicly. His friendship, however, was not a complete blessing, for he had many enemies due to his tactlessness. These enemies Balboa naturally inherited. Nor was Quevedo above reproach as a religious leader, for he made no effort to stem the terrible treatment of the natives. Instead, he encouraged gifts of slaves and stolen plunder as much as Pedrarias. Indeed, though grateful for his goodwill, Balboa sometimes regretted it as well, for it was often embarrassing. Quevedo was always at odds with the governor and by his furious partisanship on behalf of Balboa, only managed to stir the already jealous Pedrarias to further fury against him.

Conditions in Darien grew worse and worse. Pedrarias made no attempt to establish peace with the Indians nor start settlements.

The Spaniards violated every ethical code, human and religious, as they ravaged the land for gold and slaves.

Both Balboa and Quevedo wrote protests to the Spanish court, but nothing came of them. The bishop told Balboa that he suspected the letters never reached the king, but were apprehended by underling friends of Pedrarias before they reached his hands. Pedrarias also was writing letters to Ferdinand, justifying his conduct and falsifying the statements of Balboa. Having influence at court, his words rather than Balboa's were given credence.

Balboa, unable to believe King Ferdinand would continue to be indifferent to the corruption in Darien, wrote him another letter in the fall of 1515.

Most Christian and Most Puissant Lord: In the month of April I wrote Your Majesty a letter and two others before that time, informing Your Royal Highness of the things that have passed here since the coming of the Governor Pedrarias Dávila with the armada and also asking that Your Majesty send a person here who should learn of all the things which have happened until now, because the land is in such a state that it is necessary for the service of Your Royal Highness to provide some remedy before all is lost. For the affairs here are in such condition that the person who would put them back into the state in which they used to be must neither sleep nor be careless. Whereas the caciques and Indians were formerly like lambs, they have now become fierce lions, and are very bold. In other times they used to come forth upon the roads with presents for the Christians, but now they come forth to attack and to kill them boldly. And all this is because of the evil treatment accorded them in the raids which the captains made, and in the destruction dealt to many caciques and Indians without any cause or reason for it, and the robberies which they committed against them, not stopping with taking away their possessions, but also their women and children, young and old, by which God Our Lord has been evilly served and Your Majesty also. . .

For this reason there is neither a peaceful cacique nor Indian in all this land, unless it is the Cacique Careta, who is still friendly because he is so near this place. . .

With respect to the Governor, although an honorable person, Your Highness must know that he is very old for this country and that he is very ill of a serious disease, insomuch that he has not been well for a single day since he arrived. He is excessively impatient and would not care much if half his followers were lost in the raids. . . He is a man who is much pleased to see discord between one and another and when it does not exist he causes it by speaking evil to one man of another, and this is a very prominent vice of his. He is a man absorbed in his profits and greed, who forgets that he is Governor, and gives attention to nothing else, and it makes no difference to him if everyone is lost, as if he were not Governor. . . He is a man who more easily believes evil things than good, or those that will bring him some profit. . . And what I beg of Your Highness, so that you will not consider me a slanderer, is that you send some one to get information of what I say, from all the people who come from these parts, and Your Highness will clearly see that all that I have said is the truth. . .

But before Ferdinand could make an attempt to remedy matters in Darien, he died and for two years thereafter, from 1515 to 1517, affairs in Spain were in turmoil and things were so uncertain that the colony of Darien was well-nigh forgotten. The undeserving Pedrarias, therefore, wielded unhindered his treacherous staff of authority.

Balboa, still restricted as to his movements and under the cloud of his continued residencia, was soon further outraged to learn that Pedrarias and his minions were conspiring to give his command of settling the South Sea shores to another, Diego de Albítez, who was once in his own service but now a favorite with Pedrarias.

Although Quevedo refused to sign this request, in November 1515, Enciso sailed for Spain with the document with which he hoped to bring about the complete undoing of his ancient enemy, Vasco Núñez de Balboa.

Balboa determined to assert his rights. Secretly, a few loyal friends gathered in his little cabin. Windows and doors were shut and the only light was a fragment of candle, carefully preserved for the occasion.

He set his plan before them, looking from one to another earnestly as he spoke. There weren't many left, he thought ironically, who dared to meet him even in secret. Rodrigo Pérez, an honest friar. Andrés de Valderrábano, his notary when he had discovered the South Sea, Fernando Múñoz. Luis Botello. Hernando de Argüello. And — Andrés Garavito.

"I am determined to delay no longer," said Balboa, "but to take possession of those lands granted to me by the king. But for such an undertaking I need money, a ship, and men."

"We'll help you raise the money," cried Hernando de Argüello.

Andrés Garavito was chosen to go to Cuba to buy a vessel and recruit volunteers for the proposed expedition. Pedrarias was away at Aclá at the time, where he was once more attempting to establish a settlement. Before going, he had left strict orders that Balboa was not to move from the colony and was to be closely watched.

In a short time, Garavito returned with a well-armed shipload of resolute adventurers. He anchored about six leagues from the harbor and sent word to Vasco Núñez de Balboa that all was ready.

However, just as Balboa set out to join him, the unexpected happened. Pedrarias returned from Aclá! He had been taken ill and had decided to return to Darien. Enraged that Balboa had gone ahead without his permission, he promptly arrested him.

" 'Tis nothing less than revolt!" he stormed. Not content with mere imprisonment, he ordered a wooden cage built in his own house for the despairing adelantado.

Once again, however, the bishop intervened and persuaded Pedrarias that no treason nor mutiny against his authority had been intended. Weakened from illness, the governor at last wearily consented to Balboa's release. Quevedo, finding the ruler more tractable than usual, introduced a plan he had long been considering.

"This Vasco Núñez de Balboa," he said, "is a dangerous enemy, but he might make you a strong ally if you wished."

Pedrarias' bitter laughter turned to violent coughing. He raised bloodshot eyes to the bishop.

"You would jest upon a man's deathbed, Quevedo," he rasped.

"I do not jest. You are old and unwell, Pedrarias — and no one grows younger. The friendship of Vasco Núñez de Balboa would be to your advantage."

Pedrarias lay back on his pillows and closed his eyes. "Do not weary me with this nonsense, Quevedo. You must know how impossible it would be to make a friend of that impudent rascal."

"It is not impossible," answered the bishop impatiently. "Give him your eldest daughter in marriage."

Pedrarias struggled to a sitting position, his eyes staring.

"This alliance would not fail to advance your administration. Instead of a rival, you would have a son-in-law. While he labored, you could superintend matters and take your ease."

"But — but — " sputtered the amazed Pedrarias.

"He is, moreover, of noble birth and has been elevated by the title of adelantado. The match would not be beneath you. Think what a wise thing it would be for you to do."

Pedrarias thought, and was forced to admit the truth of the bishop's arguments.

"Mm. I will speak of this matter to my wife," he told Quevedo gruffly. "I will let you know."

Doña Isabella, always kindly toward Balboa, was in favor of the match. Next, Quevedo went to broach the subject to Balboa, whose first reaction was incredulity.

"But I have a wife!" he protested. "True, we were never wed in church, but Indian rites bound me to her."

The bishop smiled deprecatingly. "She is but a native woman. No holy contract binds you."

Balboa's face grew graven. "Love is holy and therefore I am bound."

Quevedo gulped his astonishment at this blind stubbornness. "Don't you realize what this alliance will mean to you? Your feud with Pedrarias will end. You will have peace. You will be able to take advantage of all your privileges as adelantado and captain of the South Sea. You can explore your lands and establish your colonies and Pedrarias will aid rather than hinder you."

Balboa had longed for this very opportunity, but not at such a price. Turn from Luaia whose quiet loyalty had never wavered in the dark days of adversity? Turn from her to a woman whom he had never seen, far away in a convent in Spain? Turn from his Indian princess to a daughter of the despicable Pedrarias?

Yet he thought with longing of the opportunities which would be his at last. He would be free to seek those glorious lands of which he had dreamed night and day. He would be able, perhaps, to undo some of the wrongs of Pedrarias' rule, make friends again with the natives, establish peace, prove to his sovereign his worthiness.

But Luaia? Luaia?

"No," he said. "Tell Pedrarias I will not marry his wretched daughter. Tell him I would rather rot from inaction than enter into such a hypocritical alliance."

"If I tell him that, Vasco Núñez," said the bishop soberly, "your days will be numbered. If she loves you, your native girl would rather see you betrothed to another than to see you slain."

It was true. Pedrarias would receive his refusal as a gross insult and would not hesitate to avenge himself to the utmost for this defiance. Balboa pushed his fingers through his hair, perspiration beading his face.

"Give me a few hours to think it over," he said. "Just a few hours."

CHAPTER XXXIII

SHIPS FOR THE SOUTH SEA

IT WAS THE INDIAN PRINCESS HERSELF WHO FINALLY PERSUADED Balboa to accept the hand of Pedrarias' absent daughter. Clinging to him, she assuaged the agony of his indecision with her quiet words and steadfastness.

"Vas-co, you must not refuse. This girl, she is far across the waters. Perhaps she will never come at all."

Balboa's mind grasped at this possibility. Aye, perhaps this Doña María would never come to Terra Firma. Even if she did, it would be months, perhaps years before she arrived, and much might happen. In the meantime, it might be that he could raise himself to such prominence that he might be able, when the time came, to free himself from the empty vows which circumstances forced upon him. Certainly such a course would cause Doña María no suffering, for her heart was as uninvolved as his own.

Therefore in April, 1516, Vasco Núñez de Balboa submitted to the betrothal rites. The entire ceremony seemed unreal and incredible to him. He found it difficult to think that this would end the bitter feud between Pedrarias and himself. Certainly the governor had not undergone any vital change, nor had he. Trying to grapple with the whys and wherefores of the confusing problem was like trying to traverse a treacherous and unfamiliar marsh. Finally, unable to convince his forthright self of the logic of the matter, he abandoned the puzzle entirely. He would deal with it when the time came.

A surface harmony now reigned. Pedrarias considered Balboa his son-in-law and bestowed upon him all the favors which he should have received long since. They immediately began to make plans for the establishment of a base for subsequent expeditions to the South Sea. Balboa favored Nombre de Dios because it was nearer the South Sea, but Pedrarias insisted that since he had already started a settlement at Aclá, that must be completed. The governor, Balboa saw, did not wish to yield the prestige of having been the first to start a colony out of Darien, as his late monarch had desired. Therefore, anxious to preserve peace, Balboa agreed. After the building of Aclá was finished, Pedrarias said, Balboa could construct four brigantines for his exploration of the southern ocean.

The settlement which Pedrarias had started at Aclá and left under the charge of Lope de Olano had been completely wiped out by Indians who sought revenge for the atrocities committed by the former follower of Nicuesa. Vasco Núñez, as a result, must begin all over again and among hostile natives. Moreover, he was given less than a hundred men, including those whom Garavito had enlisted in Cuba, because most of the soldiers were with Espinosa on another expedition seeking gold.

The first of the year in 1517, Balboa and his men sailed. The adelantado had been advanced some money from the royal treasury and Hernando de Argüello, who had become wealthy, augmented the sum.

"What better investment could I make?" he asked laughingly. "I have long been an admirer of your ability, Vasco Núñez. Consider it as a token of my regard."

"You shall not lose by it, Hernando," said Balboa gratefully. "I will see that you profit." He put his hands on his friend's shoulders. "I wish that you were coming along to Aclá."

"I, too. But you need true friends here in Darien as well — to let you know which way the wind blows." He shrugged in the direction of Pedrarias' dwelling.

"The wind has never blown more favorably for me." Balboa smiled. "Give over your suspicions, Hernando. We are done with such things, and must throw off the habit of gloom."

Hernando said slowly: "I suppose so. Nevertheless —"

"Nevertheless, if your keen ears and eyes detect aught amiss in Darien, I shall appreciate a communication from you."

He embraced the loyal notary, and went off down the path toward the ship. Luaia was waiting for him, for she had begged to be taken with him to Aclá.

"It is long since I have seen my father," she said. "If it is true, as they say, that it was his people who fell upon the force of Lope de Olano, I may be able to speak with him and assure him that you intend to respect his rights and maintain friendship."

"Aye, so you may," agreed Balboa. "But —"

"Ai-ee, do not leave me at Darien," she pleaded. "I wish to share your life, wherever you are."

In the end, he consented.

At Aclá, Balboa began with a light heart to repair the town. Restored hope gave new vigor to his work and his dauntless enthusiasm was caught by his men who labored with a will.

Espinosa, returning from his expedition, passed through Aclá and was greatly surprised to find how much Balboa had accomplished in the two months he had been there.

"We did not expect to find even water here," he told Balboa admiringly, "for we had heard of the fate of Lope de Olano's force."

Indeed, life at Aclá was harmonious and orderly. Crops were planted, dwellings erected, measures of safety taken. Espinosa and his men were given nourishing food and treated with every hospitality available before continuing their journey to Darien.

"I shall take pleasure in reporting your remarkable progress to Pedrarias," said Espinosa in parting. "He should be well-pleased with his future son-in-law."

The colonial buildings completed, Balboa commenced work on his brigantines. However, he soon found that more men were needed for the task, so he went back to Darien to secure them.

Pedrarias, however, now announced that he himself was going to undertake the expedition to the South Sea. Balboa was aghast at this violation of the agreement between them. Again he found a champion in Quevedo, who protested to the council with all his customary vim. The council, for once, was disposed to agree with him. More and more, they had become aware of Pedrarias' failings as a leader. A recent expedition of the governor's to Cenú had failed utterly, as had his previous attempt to establish a base at Aclá. Though the members of the council were still not particularly friendly to Balboa, they recognized his ability. If he led an expedition, he would bring back wealth which, according to law, must be shared with them.

Therefore the council persuaded Pedrarias that his health would suffer from such a hard journey and that his person was much too valuable to risk. They suggested that the command be given to Factor Tavira, an official, Vasco Núñez de Balboa and Captain Diego de Albítez.

Pedrarias reluctantly consented. He gave Balboa two hundred men and additional materials for the construction of the ships, as well as thirty negroes brought from Española. Needing further assistance, Balboa formed the South Sea Company in which many settlers favorable to him invested. Hernando de Argüello put all he had into the venture, so certain was he of its success under Balboa's guidance. He also agreed to act as Balboa's agent in Darien.

All was well, except for one unreasonable stipulation made by Pedrarias — that the undertaking should be completed by February, 1518. Only seven months to build ships, establish the proposed base at Isla Rica in the southern ocean and to finish his exploration there!

Balboa, however, gave little thought to the time limit, for he was possessed with great confidence and determination. Nothing could hinder him now, he assured himself. Fortune at last was favoring him.

The task of constructing the ships was a gigantic one. At Aclá timber was felled to be transported across the isthmus, together with the rigging and anchors, there to be built into ships and launched on the South Sea. The Indian paths over which the backbreaking burdens were to be carried were narrow and rocky, straggling through the green resisting jungle, across rushing streams, over mountain precipices and, finally, down to the shore of the ocean. The tropical sun, burning down upon the naked backs of the men, was almost intolerable and many of the Indians, unaccustomed to such hard labor, succumbed.

Scarcely had work begun upon the timber when a terrible discovery was made. The wood was ravaged by worms and so was useless. Refusing to be discouraged, Balboa remembered that on one occasion Careta had mentioned a wood so bitter that worms would not attack it. Searching, he found these trees on the land near the river named Rio de las Balsas. Here a post was established, for the river was capable of floating the brigantines down to the southern sea.

In six months the work was well under way and much had

been accomplished, but the time limit set by Pedrarias was almost up. Balboa, therefore, wrote to Argüello in Darien asking that he intercede with the governor for a time extension in order to finish the work he had so ably started.

Pedrarias and his council were opposed to giving Balboa additional time and wanted to relieve him of his command. Quevedo again protested so vigorously that they were forced to give in, although only to the extent of four months, obviously not time enough. It was known that the bishop planned to return soon to Spain, and Pedrarias feared that unless he conceded to some of his requests, Quevedo's report to the court was likely to be very unfavorable to himself.

Late in January, 1518, Quevedo departed for Spain, confident that all was well with the man whom he had continually championed. The adelantado, he was convinced, was now in a position to look after himself. Balboa also felt confident of this.

Leaving Aclá to join the men at the fort on the river bank of Rio de la Balsas, Balboa was courageously certain of ultimate success. The sun blazed overhead; the air here in this mountainous region was fresher and more healthful than in the lowlands of Darien. A breath of it was like the air of Xeres de los Caballeros, and the dreams of his youth grew strong again in his soul. Anything was possible — anything good. The forces of evil fired by the envy of Pedrarias had abated. Here he was surrounded by loyal followers and close friends.

Only one thing blew like a gray cobweb across his happiness. A small thing — trivial in itself.

He had returned to his cabin in Aclá the day before to find Luaia quivering with fear and indignation.

"Ai-ee," she wailed, "I am glad you are back!"

"What has happened?"

Her red lips curled back from her strong white teeth. Revulsion flared in her eyes.

"That Garavito — he came here."

"Here?" puzzled Balboa. "What for?"

"To see me."

"You!"

"He — how do you say it in Spanish? — made the advances to me. That dog with the eyes of a cat!"

Balboa stood like a stone — a stone heated in a terrible fire. So Andrés Garavito still desired Careta's daughter! The years had not dimmed his passion, but had only implanted it the more deeply. The pitiful fool — did he think to come between them?

He stepped toward Luaia. "What did you do? How did you answer him?"

The little princess bowed her head. "I — I was not as you have taught me. I — I was not a lady. I raised my voice at him like a shrill jungle parrot. I told him that he was the brother of worms that riddled the ship's wood. I told him he was a lizard living in mud. I told him —"

"And did he leave then?" asked Vasco Núñez, a faint smile taking the grimness from his mouth.

"He left," she nodded. Then her hands clutched him tightly. "He left, Vas-co, but there was bad promise in his eyes. Ai-ee, I am afraid. Do not ever leave me."

Seeking out Andrés Garavito, Balboa rebuked him sharply.

Garavito's eyes dropped. "I did not know. I thought perhaps you — you had tired of her. She is only a native, after all, and I supposed —"

"You supposed wrong, Andrés. If your imagining that you could win her was not so completely ridiculous, I would break you, bone by bone." He sighed and shook his head. "This violation of our long friendship, Andrés, grieves me much."

Garavito's voice came low and forced. "I ask your pardon," he said in apparent humility. "Henceforth I will remember that as long as she is yours, she cannot be mine."

Balboa, ever quick to forgive, put a hand on his shoulder.

"Aye, remember that henceforth, and I shall dismiss the matter from my thoughts."

Balboa took Luaia with him to the fort at Rio de las Balsas, for she pleaded, as at Darien, not to be left behind. Soon many difficulties took his attention.

The change of season brought the rains and the river began to rise alarmingly. Suddenly, without warning, it was flooding its banks. Men working on parts of the ships hurriedly climbed trees to save their lives, while the precious woods were swept away. Valiantly they set to work again. This time famine distressed them, and they were forced, as many times past, to eat roots and vegetation.

Nearly despairing, with only two months remaining for completion of the great undertaking, Balboa sent to Darien for aid. Sixty men were sent from Santa María, together with supplies and assurance of future help, if necessary.

At last, in the spring of 1518, two brigantines sailed down the river into the southern ocean, where they set out for Isla Rica. Here they established a base.

Late in June Balboa wrote to Argüello to ask Pedrarias again for additional time. In December, six months later, he still had heard nothing from the Darien colony. No answer had come from letters he had written to Argüello or Pedrarias.

It was while he was thus disturbed at lack of news that a rumor came from Aclá. A new governor, it was said, was being sent from Spain to supersede Pedrarias!

CHAPTER XXXIV

"I MYSELF GO IN FRONT"

At one time, the news of the appointment of a new governor would have pleased Vasco Núñez de Balboa greatly. Now, however, he considered himself on friendly terms with Pedrarias. Another governor might have his own favorites and might even give his command of the South Sea expedition to another.

Driven by this new anxiety, he sent for a few trusted friends. They were the priest, Rodrigo Pérez; Fernando Múñoz; Luis Botello; Andrés de Valderrábano, the notary, and finally, Andrés Garavito, whom Balboa had completely forgiven.

"We must send someone to Aclá," said Balboa, "to find out if this rumor is true."

"Aye," nodded Andrés Garavito immediately, "someone must go in secret."

"A servant in the adelantado's house will know," suggested Andrés de Valderrábano.

"If the rumor is untrue," said Balboa, "then we have nothing to worry about. Simply send a request to Pedrarias for additional supplies and more time for the undertaking. He will surely grant them."

"But if it is true?" asked Luis Botello, his eyes troubled.

"Then we must not stand stupidly by and see the command of the adelantado given to another!" shouted Andrés Garavito.

"Nay, we must not!" cried Fernando Múñoz.

"Instead, let us put to sea immediately," said Luis Botello, jumping excitedly to his feet.

Balboa looked from one to the other. "That might look like treason," he said slowly.

"Nonsense," said Garavito, his eyes smoldering under the thick spread of his lashes. "It is the course of a bold man, I admit, but it is no treason to Spain."

The priest, Rodrigo Pérez, nodded. "He is right. It is a bold course, but the only one."

"But whom shall we send?" asked Balboa.

"I will go right willingly," offered Andrés Garavito.

"It will be dangerous, should you be caught," warned Balboa.

"Nevertheless I want to go. I — I am anxious to — to make amends for certain things," he said, so low that only Balboa's ears could hear the words. "Besides," he said more loudly, "I am taken with one of the servants of your house, Vasco Núñez. The little maid Fulvia. I would be glad of this opportunity to see her."

The men laughed uproariously at this admission. Balboa's heart thudded with relief. Luaia was safe here with him at Isla Rica, and if it were true that Garavito cared for the maid, Fulvia, then he would no longer annoy Luaia.

"Very well, Andrés, you may go to Aclá," agreed Balboa. "But take care not to be caught, for that would be fatal to our plans, should the rumor prove true."

"I know that," said Andrés Garavito.

Time passed and no word from Garavito. Balboa did not allow himself to be too worried. Any number of things, he reasoned with characteristic optimism, might be delaying him. He might have gone on to Darien for supplies, or might be waiting at Aclá to confirm the rumor.

Moreover, life at Isla Rica was good. Balboa felt at home in

the wilderness and at peace on the island of the great sea he
had discovered. Here, once more, he was in supreme command
of a band of hardy adventurers. Yet he was more than a
leader. He was a companion — working, laughing, dreaming
with his men.

One night Vasco Núñez joined a group upon the moonlit
beach. The sky was cloudless. The brilliant stars seemed
drawn near the earth, as if trying to impart some ancient secret
to those on the darkened planet — or so Balboa fancied, his
imagination active.

He lay upon his back, his clasped hands cushioning his head,
his eyes idly examining the shining heavens. Where was the
star the astrologer, Micer Codro, had said was his? He had
not thought of it in years. Indeed, he had had no time. Now
where was that bit of shining mystery?

His searching eyes found it, widening. Could it be? His
heart beat more strongly as he checked its position in the firma-
ment. Aye, there could be no mistake. The star was at the
place Micer Codro had said would indicate a period of great
peril for him. He remembered the Venetian's words.

"When your star reaches that point in the heavens, beware,
Vasco Núñez de Balboa. That will be a time of greatest peril.
Should you survive, however, you will become rich and pow-
erful — the strongest captain in these lands."

Balboa sat up, laughing heartily, to tell his companions about
the amusing coincidence.

"What nonsense these astrologers mouth! I have never been
in less peril in my life. I am healthy. I have four brigantines
and three hundred loyal soldiers for my exploring expeditions.
I am the most fortunate of men!"

The next day a letter was brought by a messenger from
Pedrarias. The governor was at Darien and would like an

interview with the adelantado so that they might arrange for the necessary supplies and discuss plans for the forthcoming voyages on the southern ocean.

Unsuspecting, Balboa and his chief officers set out for Aclá at once, escorted by the messenger. They had traversed the mountains and were in sight of the settlement when the messenger drew Balboa aside.

"In all humanity, I cannot let such a gallant man proceed without warning."

"Warning? Of what?"

"Pedrarias means to arrest you upon your arrival. That I know."

"But his letter — "

"Was but to lure you, unsuspecting. Andrés Garavito was taken, and has confessed a plot."

"But I plotted not against Pedrarias!"

"Your willingness to return to Aclá without the protection of an armed force has convinced me of that. Your actions are those of innocence."

"Then if you realize that, surely the governor will."

The man shook his head dubiously. "He is enraged because of Andrés Garavito's incriminating confession."

"Then the confession was not true. When Pedrarias sees me and hears my explanation, he will no longer harbor suspicions of my intentions."

"Do not depend upon that," begged the messenger. "There is yet time to return to your ships and sail away to freedom."

"What, and be accused of rebellion against Spain? Nay, if I did so, it would be to give Pedrarias actual grounds for believing in my guilt." He lifted his head, his resolute gaze on the faraway cluster below that was the colony of Aclá. "Let us continue our journey."

Less than a league further an armed force approached, led by Francisco Pizarro who, in an arrogant tone, ordered Balboa's arrest.

Balboa stepped back, his eyes grieving. "Do you receive me thus, Francisco — after all we have suffered as comrades together?"

"I have my orders," said Pizarro haughtily. His eyes were hard and would not meet Balboa's.

"Then I will not make it difficult for you to carry them out, Francisco," said Balboa quietly.

He allowed himself to be manacled and led to Aclá like a dangerous criminal. He was placed in the settlement's strongest building and closely guarded.

Pedrarias came to visit him, and blamed the treasurer, Alonzo de la Puente, for the unpleasant situation. "He has brought charges against you," said the governor smoothly, "and has insisted on an investigation. For myself, I do not doubt your loyalty, my son."

Balboa was placed on trial for treasonable conspiracy against the crown. To his amazement, it was Andrés Garavito who testified against him, swearing before all that Vasco Núñez de Balboa had plotted to seize entire control of all the lands of the southern sea.

Sadly, Balboa realized that Andrés Garavito hated him, had never felt the friendship he professed. When the trial was over, Balboa was taken back to prison, along with Luis Botello, Andrés de Valderrábano, Fernando Múñoz, Rodrigo Pérez — and, finally, Hernando de Argüello. Argüello had attempted to warn Balboa of Pedrarias' intentions and to urge him to flee by setting sail in one of his ships. This letter, Balboa learned, had been intercepted by Pedrarias and had further aroused his suspicions.

On January 12, 1519, the verdict was given. The adelantado, Vasco Núñez de Balboa, was pronounced guilty and condemned to death. Argüello, Múñoz, Botello and Valderrábano were sentenced to follow him to the block. Only Rodrigo Pérez was pardoned, since he was a priest — and Andrés Garavito, who was amply rewarded, as well, for his aid in securing his comrade's conviction.

It was dark when they were led back to prison. The night sky was overcast. Neither moon nor stars lightened the dismal room. The faces of the five men were pale blurs in the gloom. Outside the guards walked back and forth with heavy tread.

"I have been proud to lead such men as you," groaned Balboa at last, "but I never thought to lead you to your execution."

Thick silence stretched between them. Then Hernando de Argüello spoke softly.

"Do not reproach yourself, Vasco Núñez. There is no man I would rather follow upon the greatest of all adventures."

"Aye," put in Luis Botello gruffly, "all men must die sooner or later — and none could choose more gallant company."

"But the injustice of it tears at me!" cried Fernando Múñoz. "We be innocent of the treason charged to us."

"Innocent men have been executed before," said Andrés de Valderrábano.

"There was one who died upon a cross," Balboa remembered. Humility filled his heart.

"Aye, martyrdom but serves to increase the glory of a great name," said Hernando de Argüello. "And yours is a great name, Vasco Núñez de Balboa. Perhaps we all shall obtain immortality because we died with you."

"I verily believe it," said Luis Botello staunchly.

Wonder growing in his soul, Vasco Núñez stared into the darkness. Surely this was a loyalty beyond that of men. No doubt God had bestowed it on these steadfast comrades to bring comfort in this hour. They were not afraid to die with their leader, they said. Well, neither did he fear to perish with such valorous men. Perhaps this was, as Hernando de Argüello had said, the greatest of all adventures. As such, he would face it on the morrow.

There was a small sound at the window, his name whispered. Balboa rose and drew near.

"Fulvia!"

The little maid wept softly. "The guard let me by for a moment. Is there nothing I can do to help you, dear master?"

Briefly, Balboa shut his eyes in thanks to God. Here was the answer to his prayer — a way to send a message to Luaia.

"Can you get a message to your mistress at Isla Rica?"

Fulvia nodded, gulping back her sobs.

"Tell her," said Vasco Núñez earnestly, "to return to her father as she once promised. She will be safe there." He leaned closer to the little native maid. "Tell her this, too — that my spirit will be with her always."

"I will tell her," promised Fulvia. "Ai-ee, master, my heart grieves for you!"

"Do not grieve," said Balboa gently.

"Come away now!" barked the guard, approaching.

Fulvia's little hand fluttered through the window to touch her master's face. Then she was gone.

Balboa remained where he was. The wind had risen and he could feel the freshness of it on his face. Oddly, he was no longer plagued by the great wrong being done him. His time was done, but many blessings had been his. He had known great love, steadfast friendship, and glorious achievement.

More than all else, he had been given that moment of towering splendor when his eyes had first beheld the great southern sea. The thunderous shining of it had become a part of his being.

Aye, God had made him a pathfinder in the wilderness, a discoverer of the great glories wrought by His hands, a leader of gallant men.

Proudly he would go forth on the morrow, even as he had once written to his king:

"I myself go in front of them, whether it might be by night or day . . ."

AFTERWARD

BUT WHAT OF THE STRUGGLING COLONY AFTER THE GALLANT leader marched to the headsman's block, there to meet death as bravely as he had challenged life? What of the vast New World, the shores of the great South Sea he had discovered? What of the brown-skinned natives, breaking under the lash of cruelty no longer stemmed? What of the great conquistador's enemies whose deeds wreathe in black his golden memory? Whose dark names live only because of the brightness of his? What of Pedrarias, Enciso, and the traitor, Garavito?

At the Spanish court, Balboa's staunch friend, Oviedo, was tireless in his denunciations of Pedrarias. Finally his complaints bore fruit. A new governor, Lope de Sosa, was appointed to replace Pedrarias. He did not arrive in the Indies until May, 1520 — too late to save Vasco Núñez de Balboa. With this new governor was a judge, Juan Rodriguez de Alarconcillo, whom the king had ordered to subject Pedrarias to a residencia.

It seemed that Pedrarias' days of power were ending. But not so. Lope de Sosa was suddenly stricken with a mysterious illness while still on board ship anchored in the harbor. He died without ever coming ashore to Terra Firma. How great must have been Pedrarias' inward rejoicing! Saved by fate — or were there whisperings of another hand in the new governor's death? Some follower of Pedrarias aboard ship, perhaps, to manage things conveniently?

Whatever his thoughts, Pedrarias masked them well. He mourned with all the ardor of a hypocrite. He staged an elaborate funeral for his would-have-been successor. Great homage the old man paid the dead! Solemn and long drawn out were the rites with which the body was interred before the altar of Santa María's church!

With Lope de Sosa disposed of so neatly, Pedrarias set about winning Judge Alarconcillo. He offered the magistrate the same salary and position in his own court which he would have had under De Sosa. Flattery and lavish gifts soon won Alarconcillo over. He wrote at once for permission from the Spanish court to serve under Pedrarias. And that, the governor doubtless smiled, took care of the possible discomforts of the residencia. However, perhaps it would do no harm to make sure. Therefore he sent his wife, gracious Doña Isabella, back to the Spanish court with a great quantity of gold and pearls. She was to have Alarconcillo's appointment verified and to see that Pedrarias remained, unmolested, in his present position of governor.

It was easy. Don Carlos, the emperor, was traveling at the time and Pedrarias' fellow villain, Bishop Juan de Fonseca, held sway at Court. Smoothly and quietly, matters were settled, with the aid of the treasure sent by Pedrarias.

The following July, the residencia was held. The governor magnanimously invited all who had complaints against him to make them. Naturally, as he well knew, no one dared present charges. Balboa's fate was not easily forgotten, nor Pedrarias' many other atrocities, nor his vindictiveness, nor the fact that Alarconcillo was now his fast friend and follower. Foolhardy, indeed, would the man have been who dared lift his voice against the powerful governor! The result of the investigation? Pedrarias vindicated, of course. His rule approved. No mention of Vasco Núñez de Balboa, his farcical trial and hasty execution.

But back in Spain there was one who remembered, who cried out against injustice as his brother would have done. Gonzalo Balboa had not seen his famous big brother, Vasco, since he himself was but a lad. Yet he could not forget the flaming high-held head, the great frame, the piercing level blue of eyes, the firm but kindly mouth. His hero, Vasco, a traitor? The name of Balboa besmirched? He could not go his way. He could not walk the roads of Spain in peace unless the wrong were righted and the blot upon his brother's name royally erased.

So to the emperor he went, fearless like his brother. Vasco Núñez de Balboa, he said, kneeling at his sovereign's feet, had not been guilty of treason, but had been the victim of Pedrarias' malice. There were character witnesses who would not hesitate to bear him out. Oviedo, for one. Rodrigo Pérez, the pardoned priest, sent off to Spain in chains and now honorably released. Others, too, many of them residents of Balboa's colony when he was governor. Let them speak.

And speak they did, with the name of Vasco Núñez de Balboa like a flame upon their loyal lips. A blazing fire in their eyes. A firmness in their manner.

The emperor was convinced. He issued a decree granting Gonzalo's petition for Balboa's possessions, confiscated by Pedrarias as the property of a convicted traitor. His majesty spoke also of Balboa's great contribution to Spain and his devoted service to the crown. And still — after all that — he made no effort to punish Pedrarias for what his own words indicated amounted to murder. Juan de Fonseca? There can be little doubt of it. His influence here is plain as black writing on parchment. "Let retribution go, your Majesty. Pedrarias erred, perhaps — but only through loyalty to the crown. His intentions were beyond reproach. Too late now to bring Bal-

boa back. Pedrarias is a strong and wily ruler — and a strong
hand is needed in those wild lands beyond the sea. Let retribution go."

Pedrarias, receiving the order to restore Balboa's property,
simply ignored it. Comply with it? He would then be admitting himself wrong in executing Balboa. That was one thing
he would never do — admit himself in error. It was a sword-
sharp rule he lived by. Though others were cut to pieces by it,
thus he preserved himself and his career. So Gonzalo Balboa
waited in vain for the property of his glorious martyred brother.

There can be little doubt, however, that Balboa's name was
cleared entirely of the taint of treason. For in 1522, his good
friend and comrade, Rodrigo Pérez, the priest, was sent back to
Castillo del Oro, promoted to the office of arch-deacon!

But what of Pedrarias? The outrages of his rule increased.
Oviedo, who had returned to the colony with the ill-fated Lope
de Sosa, remained for some time, abhorring the rottenness of
the old governor, hating his greed, despising his cruelties, the
enslavement and murder of the helpless natives. Protesting
these, he soon found himself marked for assassination, but managed to return to Spain. Again he presented charges against
Pedrarias. His efforts sent Pedro de los Rios across the seas to
be the new governor and with him a judge, as before, to order
a residencia. This was in 1526.

But Pedrarias' adroit wife saved him once more. Through
her an order was signed that the second residencia should ap-
ply only to happenings since the first! Thus Balboa's death
remained officially uninvestigated.

Pedrarias' politic wife also secured for him the government
of the neighboring and recently subjugated territory of Nica-
ragua. Though replaced as governor of Castilla del Oro, he
actually was advanced rather than demoted. In his new dis-

trict he continued to live as he pleased, which was, apparently, to make the lives of others as miserable as possible. Those who stood in his way he removed, by beheading or by poison. Naked Indians armed only by wooden staves were thrown to starving vicious hounds — these exhibitions as a kind of recreation for this Spanish Nero. Indeed, the reign of Pedrarias is probably the bloodiest in the New World. No doubt, conquistadors who followed Balboa, marching through the western gateway he had discovered, took their cue from the old governor. They had become hardened to blood and destruction and death. Greed became virtue. Deception, intelligence. Violence, they considered, a necessity. Pedrarias had taught them well, with many an example to harden their hearts and stunt their manhood. For, according to the historian, Oviedo, two million Indians and more met their deaths during Pedrarias' rule in Terra Firma, a span of sixteen years.

How passed the wickedness that was Pedrarias? And when? Did he die violently and in agony? No. His was a peaceful passing, accompanied by the last rites of the Church, as he lay in his luxurious bed at León, his capital, in 1531. But was he then so hardened that there did not come at the last moment some choking regret, a sudden strangling fear? History has no answer.

The betrayer, Andrés Garavito, died a year before Pedrarias to whom he had delivered Balboa. Pedrarias was properly grateful for Garavito's service and rewarded him amply. Eventually, Garavito became one of Pedrarias' foremost officers — not really surprising, for they were made of the same stuff. He was honored by the emperor in 1525 for his "services to the crown" and lived the life of a favorite in the governor's retinue. He died swiftly, and apparently of heart failure, in a mock tilting contest at Aclá in 1530.

Espinosa, who had brought in the verdict against Balboa, was given the explorer's ships. He ravaged the coast in them, seizing great quantities of native gold and pearls. Very wealthy, he went back to Spain to be given a coat of arms, then returned to Terra Firma. He died at the age of seventy, in 1537, at the town of Cuzco.

Bachelor Enciso, whose venom was greatly responsible for Balboa's downfall, wrote his *Suma de Geografia* back in Spain, which earned him some renown, since it was the first book about the New World to be published there. Returning to the Indies, he died naturally in his old age, as did Puente and the Bachelor Corral.

Only one man, who played an important part in the tragedy of Vasco Núñez de Balboa who was one of the greatest and certainly the most humane of the Spanish conquistadores, remains to be accounted for. He is Francisco Pizarro, who stood beside him when the great discoverer looked for the first time at the southern sea. It was he, who, in 1532, after eight years of hardship, toiled up a mountain in the Andes — and looked down upon Peru. Another should have stood there in his stead, a great-framed, great-hearted, flame-headed man. Another should have looked with keen blue eyes upon the town of Caxamarca. He it was who dreamed of such a sight. He it was who should have realized it. And if he had — this man who believed in treaties wherever possible, who believed in native friendship rather than in enmity, knowing that without it he could never have reached the southern sea — how much less bloody would have been the Spanish conquest of the New World! So history blunders on.

BIBLIOGRAPHY

Altoguirre y Duvale, Angel de, *Vasco Núñez de Balboa,* Madrid, 1914.

Anghera, Peter Martyr de, *De Orbe Novo,* tr. from the Latin with notes by Francis Augustus MacNutt, 2 v., New York, Putnam, 1912.

Balboa, Miguel Cavello, *Histoire du Perou,* tr. from the Spanish into French by Henri Ternaux Compans, 1837–1841.

Bancroft, H. H., *History of Central America,* 2 v., San Francisco, Bancroft, 1882.

Bell, Eleanor Yorke, "The Real Panama and Its People," *Metropolitan,* Dec. 1908, also "The Republic of Panama and its people with special reference to the Indians," *Smithsonian Institution Annual Report,* Washington, 1910.

Brady, Cyrus Townsend, "Panama and a Forgotten Romance," in "Dramatic History of South America," *Cosmopolitan,* June, 1904.

Bidwell, C. T., *Isthmus of Panama,* 1865.

Bishop, Farnham, *Panama,* New York, Century, 1913.

Brion, Marcel, *Father of the Indians,* tr. by Coley B. Taylor, New York, Dutton, 1929.

Brantz, Mayer, *Mexico, Central America and West Indies.*

Brown, L. M. A. R., *Unknown Tribes, Uncharted Seas,* 1924.

Casas, Bartolomé de las, *Historia de las Indias,* 5 v., Madrid, 1875–76.

Carpenter, Frank George, *Lands of the Caribbean,* New York, Doubleday, 1925.

Charlevoix, Pierre F. X. de, *Histoire de l'isle Espagnole ou de S. Domingue,* 2 v., Paris, Pralard, 1731.

Columbus, Christopher, *Journal of the First Voyage to America,* ed. by Van Wyck Brooks, New York, Boni, 1924.

Davis, H. P., *Black Democracy, the Story of Haiti,* New York, Dial Press, 1928.

Enciso, Martin Fernández de, *Suma de Geografia,* Sevilla, 1530.

Encyclopedia Britannica: Articles on Balboa, Columbus, Pizarro, Panama and Santo Domingo.

Encyclopedia Italiana: Articles on Balboa, Columbus, and the voyages of Rodrigo de Bastidas, Rome, Instituto Della Encyclopedia Italiana, 1935–38.

Gaffarel, Paul, *Nunez de Balboa,* Paris, 1882.

Geographic News Bulletin: "Uncle Sam Signs New Lease with Landlord Panama," Washington, D.C., The National Geographic Society, Mar. 23, 1936, also, "Panama — the Republic, Not the Canal," Mar. 26, 1934.

Grinnell Review, The: "Panama and Its People," Jan., 1921.

Hale, Albert B., *Panama — Its People and Its Problems,* Reader, 1905.

Headley, J. T., *Darien Exploring Expedition under command of Lieutenant J. C. Strain,* New York, Harper.

Helps, Sir Arthur, *Spanish Conquest in America,* ed. with notes by M. Oppenheim, 4 v., London, Lane, 1900.

Gisborne, Lionel, *Isthmus of Darien in 1852, journal of the expedition of inquiry for the junction of the Atlantic and Pacific oceans, 1853.*

Irving, Washington, *The Life and Voyages of Christopher Columbus with those of His Companions,* 3 v., rev. ed., New York, Putnam, 1892.

Johnston, C. H. L., *Famous Discoverers and Explorers of America,* 1917.

Lyons, Martin K., "In Panama," *The Cunarder,* Nov., 1936.

Markham, Sir Clements R., "Vasco Núñez de Balboa," *Geographical Journal,* London, 1913, Vol. XLI, pp. 517-532.

Medina, J. T., *El Descubrimiento del Oceano Pacifico,* 4 v., Santiago de Chile, Imprinta Universitaria, 1914.

Moses, Bernard, *The Spanish Dependencies in South America,* 2 v., New York, Harper, 1914.

Múñoz, Juan Bautista, *Historia del Nuevo Mundo,* Madrid, 1793.

Marsh, Richard Oglesby, *White Indians of Darien,* New York, Putnam, 1934.

Oviedo y Valdés, Gonzalo Fernández de, *Historia General y Natural de las Indias, Islas y Tierra-Firme del Mar Oceano,* 4 v., Madrid, 1851–55.

Ober, Frederick A., *Vasco Núñez de Balboa,* New York, Harper, 1906.

Prescott, W. H., *History of the Conquest of Mexico,* 3 v., Philadelphia, Lippincott, 1882.

Prescott, W. H., *History of the Reign of Ferdinand and Isabella,* 3 v., Philadelphia, Lippincott, 1871.

Prescott, W. H., *History of the Conquest of Peru,* 2 v., Philadelphia, Lippincott, 1882.

Pan American Magazine, "Unlocking the Castles of Gold in Panama," Oct.–Nov., 1927.

Quintana, M. J., *Vidas de los Españoles Célebres,* Madrid, Perlado, Paez y Ca, 1914.

Richman, Irving Berdine, *The Spanish Conquerors,* Chronicles of America Series, New Haven, Yale University Press, 1919.

Strawn, Arthur, *Sails and Swords,* New York, Brentano's, 1928.

Shaw, Paul Vanorden, "Panama — a Land Divided," *The Christian Science Monitor,* Jan. 2, 1936.

Taylor, Don, as told to Gardner Bradford, "Hunting the Hairy People," *Los Angeles Times,* Oct. 30, 1932.

Verrill, A. Hyatt, *Panama, Past and Present,* New York, Dodd, Mead, 1922.

Thacher, John Boyd, *Christopher Columbus: His Life, His Works, His Remains,* 3 v., New York, Putnam, 1903–04.

Urretia, Carlos Gutierrez, *Vida y Hazañas de Vasco Núñez de Balboa,* Barcelona, 1916.